P6

VINCENT FIGGINS
TYPE SPECIMENS
1801 and 1815

VINCENT FIGGINS TYPE SPECIMENS

1801 and 1815

Reproduced in facsimile

Edited with

an introduction and notes

by

BERTHOLD WOLPE, R.D.I.

London

Printing Historical Society

© 1967, Berthold Wolpe
Published by
the Printing Historical Society
St Bride Institute
Bride Lane, London EC4
1 9 6 7

Publication No. 4

(

Printed in Great Britain
by the John Roberts Press
Clerkenwell Green
London

CONTENTS

'The good, old legible types formerly used in print are being scorned in these days (on account of the new ones being cut every day). And yet, however many new faces may be cut, when they have been forgotten and no more new ones can be imagined, the old ones will once more be produced under the pretence that they are new, as is the case with other things.'

Wolffgang Fugger[1] in 1553

INTRODUCTION

The beginning of the nineteenth century marks a turning point in the development of letter forms, already foreshadowed in the preceding century by the *Romain du Roi*[2], by the types of Fournier, Fleischmann, Baskerville, Bodoni, Bell, Didot and Martin. The earlier roman and italic printing types grew out of the tradition of the humanist manuscripts, and were, with their bracketed serifs, the literary counterpart of the imagery of the wood engraver's art. When copper engraving became the medium for book illustration, the style of lettering in the engravings changed to a more subtle form with swelling lines and thin contrasting serifs, easily produced by the engraver's burin or in etchings by the etcher's needle.

These tendencies made it necessary for the book and general printers to have at their disposal types in harmony with the new technique of intaglio engraving. This briefly is the reason why the style of printing types gradually changed in the eighteenth century.

The new fashion of bold downstrokes and very sharp serifs was not accepted without criticism. It may be apt to quote here a passage I found in a treatise dated 1796 by George Cumberland:[3] 'That drawings, which time has softened, and plates which a little use has worn, are more agreeable to the eye, when the forms they represent are correctly drawn, is an effect that many good judges feel; . . . hence it arises, that the types of *Baskerville* and *Bodoni* disturb vision; while those of *Giolito*[4] and *Aldus* repose; . . . It is not the excessive sharp dressing of types that gives them value, as many printers still seem to imagine; it is a fine form of letters, divested of every angle, neatly dressed and carefully printed; with a very dark ink, that does not partake of blue; and on a paper of yellowish tint, that makes the most agreeable book to a man of taste.'[5]

9

1. ABCDF GIKMNQRST L
2. ABCDF GIKMNQRST L
3. ABCDF GIKMNQRST L

1.re
Exem

1. abdefghikmnpqrſl tu
2. abdefghikmnpqrſl tu
3. abdefghikmnpqrſl tu

2.me
Exemp

From an engraving *Gravure en Lettre* in Diderot and d'Alembert:
Encyclopédie etc., Paris, c. 1760, showing how the engraver builds
up his letter forms in copper engraving

Similar thoughts which are of interest to us, as they point to the formative influence of copper engraving on type design, can be found in a *Speech on the Art of Printing* delivered by Citizen Sobry in the year 1800: 'The Didots were led into error by the pleasing effect made by letters engraved on copper that one sees at the bottom of prints. But such inscriptions, always very short and somewhat large at that, do not have time to tire us. One must not assume that they will be successful when used in a larger work. We know that efforts have been made, in the name of luxury, to have entire books engraved in copper, but the persistent repetition of such delicate strokes has always turned out to be fatiguing, and the books have met with little success. Nobody could read through Byrne's *Horace*[6]. It is not beside the point to observe that printing, which is only an expedient for supplementing handwriting and engraving, has ended by superseding them both where long works are concerned, and that printing owes this primacy to the regularity, continuity, clearness, and fine harmony of its strokes, qualities of which they should never have been deprived, and which it is essential to restore.'[7]

We have to make it plain that in the 1750s Baskerville, the writing master and manufacturer of japanned ware, brought elegance and brilliancy into the book page—whatever embattled critics like Cumberland may have had to say.

Baskerville's efforts were appreciated in Italy by Bodoni and in France by Didot, both of whom found their own noble solution to the problem of bringing the style of type into accord with the later eighteenth-century fashion which by then had turned to a severe classicism of form. It is symptomatic of the crossfertilization of ideas in the world of typography that Bodoni and the Didots— here so severely slated by Citizen Sobry—in their own turn exercised a strong influence on the English type founders of the period.

A valuable addition to the contemporary opinions already referred to—this time more flattering—comes from the pen of John McCreery who wrote in 1803:
'The extraordinary beauty of many of the works which have been executed by BODONI at PARMA, justly entitles him to rank with the most celebrated printers of the present day; nor can it be overlooked, that his labours have given a stimulus even to English exertion. In such estimation has his Press been held throughout

QR
RS

Four thirteen lines Pica letters from Caslon's broadsheet specimen
of 1764. Note the Q, similar to the one Figgins eventually used

Europe, that authors in distant countries, . . . have transmitted them [their works] to his care . . . Before the late successful efforts in England to bring printing to perfection, instances have occurred, when we have ourselves paid this humiliating tribute to Italian excellence.'[8]

One of the master printers who contributed to the above-mentioned 'late successful efforts in England' was Thomas Bensley, who in some of his finest books not only made use of the types of Vincent Figgins but also on the title pages mentioned their originator.

Yet the fact should not be disregarded that in this country at the same time considerable indigenous influences were at work that made their impact on the shaping of a new style of typography, a style different from that of the eighteenth century. This change swept away even the transitional style in which Vincent Figgins was brought up and to which his first types belonged. For centuries printing had meant the producing of books, and any other kind of printing was executed in the style of books. Whilst the production of books and other reading matter, such as newspapers and journals, increased vastly by the end of the eighteenth century, the dawn of the industrial revolution and the ensuing growth of trade and commerce brought new demands, and the necessity of quite different applications, to the printing trade.

Moreover the competition in the sphere of trade and mercantile development required bolder and larger types and thus the quiet world of books was influenced by the strident demands of advertising.

It may not be without interest in this context to look back for a moment to an earlier production of a bold and well-shaped type, related to the copper-engraved alphabet published by George Bickham the Younger in c. 1760. Very likely it was the exemplar William Caslon II followed in his very large placard types, issued from his foundry in the 1760s—a long time before Figgins produced his poster types. Their serif formation and Caslon's first showing of modern style aligning numerals must have served as a useful guide to all subsequent type producers.[9]

The same Bickham advertised—apart from his copybooks— inscriptions for houses, lodgings, liquors, grocery, snuff, etc. Here the engraver produced advertising matter in quantity on his rolling press. At that time no display types existed for such purposes.

Quoufque tandem abu-
tere, Catilina, patientia
noftra? quamdiu nos e-
tiam furor ifte tuus elu-
det? quem ad finem fefe
effrenata jactabit auda-
cia? nihilne te noctur-
num præfidium palatii,
nihil urbis vigiliæ, ni-
hil timor populi, ni-
hil confenfus bonorum
omnium, nihil hic mu-
ABCDEFGHIJK
LMNOPQRST
UVWXYZ

From the 1792 specimen

14

But it was not only the activities of the engravers—as already explained—which contributed to a new style in lettering, but also the efforts of the sculptors, metalworkers, sign writers and writing masters generally.[10] One can be sure that all this performance and activity in the field of lettering, not necessarily bound to old style tradition, but following more fashionable and up-to-date modes, must have created an atmosphere in which the type founders were forced to follow suit and create new letters in conformity with the taste of the period.

One of these founders was Vincent Figgins. A brief sketch of his career must suffice here as it has been dealt with already.[11] He was born in 1766, and indentured as apprentice in 1782 to the type founder Joseph Jackson who had learned this trade in the foundry of William Caslon I. For three years Figgins worked as manager of his master's firm, thus gaining valuable experience in the different departments of a letter foundry. When Jackson died in 1792 Vincent was not able—through lack of means—to acquire his master's business and therefore decided to start one of his own in Swan Yard, Holborn Bridge. He received encouragement and substantial orders straight away from distinguished master printers and publishers: from Thomas Bensley and John Nichols, as well as from the Delegates of the Oxford University Press. They all must have known him well and learned to appreciate his qualities as a reliable organiser and skilled craftsman, since they gave him commissions so soon. These first orders consisted mainly of the completion of work he had already begun as supervisor in the Jackson foundry, e.g.: a 'two-line English' (about 28 pt) for Bensley and a Greek type for the Oxford Press.

The first type specimen[12] from the new foundry, printed by Thomas Bensley possibly in the year 1792, consists only of a title page and of a single page showing of the two-line English Roman fount.[13] It matches well the same size type from the Jackson foundry, and displays the characteristics of the transitional style. I give an illustration of it (see opposite) as it does not appear in the book reproduced here in facsimile, and so as to be able to point out that it still contains the long letter s in the beginning and middle of words[14] and ligature ct, both of which became redundant by the end of the century. This innovation of not using the lower case long s and the abolition of certain tied letters was no doubt eagerly accepted by Figgins as it reduced considerably the number of letters in a fount. It actually must have saved him the cutting of more than a dozen punches for each size of type—no mean economy of time and expense for a budding type founder.

Also worth noting are the two variations of Capital letter Q; the first one in the Bodoni style also disappeared from the later specimens.

In 1793 a further specimen appeared consisting probably of five leaves: title (as before), the two-line English, a long-bodied English, and a Pica; preceded by the following introduction:

'At a period when the Art of Printing has, perhaps, arrived to a degree of excellence hitherto unknown in the annals of Literature, the improvement of Types will no doubt be generally considered as an object worthy of attention.

Vincent Figgins, having had the advantage of ten years instruction and servitude under the late ingenious Mr. Joseph Jackson (great part of which time he had the management of his Foundry), flatters himself he shall not be thought arrogant in soliciting the Patronage of the Master Printers, and other Literary Gentlemen, when he informs them that he has commenced an entire new Letter Foundry; every branch of which, with their support and encouragement, he hopes he shall be enabled to execute in the most accurate and satisfactory manner; assuring them that his best endeavours shall be exerted to complete so arduous an undertaking.

Although as yet he has but few Founts finished, he is anxious to submit a specimen for approbation. All orders he may be favoured with shall be duly attended to and punctually executed.

Space lines, to any length or thickness—Space Rules—Quotations and Justifiers—cast with expedition, and at the usual prices.

The Italics of the following Founts, with a Long Primer, Brevier and English, are in great forwardness—Specimens of which shall be printed as soon as possible. May 1793.'

In 1801 T. Bensley printed a broadsheet specimen of two-line letters cast by Vincent Figgins,[15] shown here as an inset. They range from Pica down to Minion in roman capitals, from Small Pica down to Nonpareil in open capitals, followed by Small Pica, Brevier, Nonpareil in open inclined capitals and finally Pica open with centre pearls.

16

The last type was cut by Richard Austin who supplied strikes not only to Figgins, but also to Wilson of Glasgow and to Fry. It is still being used under the name of Fry's Ornamented. None of these fine and useful types[16] appears in the 1815 specimen. But we find that on its title page the name of the type founder is set in the open type but in the two-line Pearl which is not shown on the broadsheet specimen.

It is neither necessary nor appropriate to mention here all early type productions of Figgins. The ones so far described are useful for outlining his development as a letter founder and for showing his versatility in tackling many quite different problems.

Early letter founders' type specimens belong to the same group of publications as trade catalogues, craftsmen's pattern books and fashion sheets. Their dating—sometimes an arduous task—is of a certain importance as it helps the researcher in matters of style to pinpoint the fluctuating fashions in typographic usage at any given period. However stimulating to our imagination they may be now, in their own time they were only ephemeral printing trade catalogues. As they were used in the printing office for selecting and ordering different founts of type they were much handled and well thumbed, and therefore sooner or later literally worn to shreds. For these reasons most of them have altogether disappeared. A few have survived and become useful stepping stones in a history of typographic design and technology.

The *Specimen of Printing Types, by Vincent Figgins, Letter-Founder, West Street, West Smithfield, London*, 1815, that we have selected for reproduction in facsimile is important for the many display types it contains and is of special significance because of its provenance: the successors to the Figgins foundry. It may well have been Vincent Figgins's own copy from this year. This fact gains in importance when we find that the other copies, with the date of 1815 on the title, which are available for examination, contain additional specimens produced after 1815. The copy, here reproduced in its entirety, consists of a title page and 76 leaves of specimens, these printed on one side of the paper only. The types as well as the typographic ornaments are arranged in decreasing sizes. The largest type, sixteen lines Pica, by force of its size, had to be accommodated on a folding sheet and the smallest, Nonpareil, Pearl and Diamond, were tipped in on a piece of paper

17

smaller than the page size which is approximately 9″ x 5⅞″ in the original book.

In 1808 Caleb Stower, master printer at 32 Paternoster Row, author of *The Printer's Grammar*, tells his readers in an introduction to 'specimens of modern-cut printing types', that 'the great improvement which has taken place of late years in the form of printing types, has completely superseded the Elzevir shape introduced from Holland by the celebrated Caslon, near ninety years ago. Every one must observe, with increasing admiration, the numerous and elegant founts of every size, which have with rapid succession been lately presented to the public. On the beauty, variety, or just arrangement of the . . . specimen, it is unnecessary for us to enlarge . . .'[17] He then continues:

'We regret that we are prevented from laying before our readers specimens from the foundry of Mr. Figgins. We understand, however, that in a few months Mr. F. will have fully completed his specimen.'

It actually took Mr. F. not a few months but a few years, seven years precisely, to achieve this, and the result of his endeavours is here under consideration.

There are seven copies known to us with the date of 1815 on the title; their locations are listed here as follows:

1 Author's collection
2 Typographical Library at the University Press, Oxford
3 Stephenson Blake, Typefounders, Sheffield
4 Stichting Museum Enschedé, Haarlem
5 American Typefounders' Library at Columbia University Library, New York
6 Mr W. Bentinck-Smith, Harvard University
7 Mr. Philip Hofer, Harvard University

Two of these, the Oxford and Sheffield copies, I was able to compare with my own.[18]

Once we have proved and accepted the fact that the model for our facsimile is through its provenance the original 1815 edition we ought then to try to find out what was added to this original book in subsequent years, and when.

As the year on the title page was not altered until 1821, we must conclude that some of the six remaining copies may be of any year between 1815 and 1821. The complexity of the task of producing an exact set of dates for these additions becomes even more apparent when examining the actual make-up and binding of the books. A printed book usually consists of folded sheets of 8, 16 or 32 pages. But this book is made up of single leaves[19] which were printed at Thomas Bensley's printing house most probably at different times, and very likely over a span of years from whenever the first founts of the newly cut and cast types became available from the foundry. This can be proved from our copy by the fact that papers watermarked 1799, 1808, 1813, 1814 and 1815 were used. When a book is made up of single leaves—and many specimen books of other founders were conveniently produced in the same manner—then a technique known as oversewing is employed.[20] Before the binding takes place leaves can be deleted, or their position changed without any hindrance to the typefounder who could bring his specimen up to date at will, replacing a page here by one more up to date, and deleting another one there which he thought had fallen out of favour with the printers.

Each copy had to be gathered individually, and the person who collated the books sometimes made mistakes. For example leaves are duplicated; thirteen lines Pica in the author's copy, Pica No. 3 in the Oxford copy, a page of ornaments in the Sheffield copy, and in one case a leaf was put in upside down.

On the whole a marked tendency towards the use of bolder types developed in the beginning of the nineteenth century; hence the lighter faces produced in the last decade of the previous century were discarded—however elegant they may appear to our eyes.

It was the custom of the founders to number their series of type chronologically, within one particular size of type. The knowledge of this system helps us to realise why certain earlier numbers in the series of some types are not represented in the 1815 book, their omission was no accident but a stylistic censure, so to speak, self-inflicted by the typefounder himself. In later issues of the specimen book we find these lacunae tidily filled by types equally bold or bolder than the rest, holding the numbers of the eighteenth century types which had been omitted in the 1815 edition. For instance, in the Oxford and Sheffield copies a Pica No. 1 has been added which is bolder than the Pica No. 3 which is included. It does not appear in the author's copy and must therefore be dated after 1815.

It is not necessary to give a detailed description of the book, as the facsimile can now be consulted. But in examining it carefully I would like to make certain observations on points of technique and design, and where necessary, to comment on variations in the other copies.

Many of the specimens have in common the text of the famous passage from Cicero's Catiline oration with the opening 'Quousque tandem . . .' first used by Caslon in 1734 and ever since by many typefounders.

Hansard as a printer of books could not appreciate the necessity and vogue of the newfangled display types, as the following outburst,[21] mingled with praise for Figgins, shows:

'The emulation to excel in cutting a new type of any peculiar feature, and the various fashions which, unfortunately for the printers, have been started and patronised, have left the specimen of a British letter-founder a heterogeneous compound made up of fat-faces and lean-faces, wide-set and close-set, proportioned and disproportioned, all at once crying "Quousque tandem abutere patientia nostra?" One founder, Mr. Figgins, has, however, broken the spell by showing specimens in our own *vulgar* tongue: still the "Quousque" must be partly retained in order to show, by comparison, the getting in, or driving out powers of his founts.'

The title border, a fine example of the Grecian style, is with much ingenuity made up of the following units (starting from outside): No 4 two lines English (1815), No 32 Brevier (not in the 1815 specimens), No 5 Long Primer (1814), No 21 English (not in the 1815 specimens) and No 32 Long Primer (1815). It shows that the second and fourth units must have been newly cut, but not ready to be incorporated into the 1815 book, where the English and Brevier units go just up to Nos 20 and 21 respectively.

The first section of the book is occupied by placard types. From sixteen lines Pica down to six lines Pica their captions describe them as cast in 'Mould & Matrices' which means—in my opinion—that they were cast in Sanspareil matrices. This innovation of cutting matrices directly, without punches, was introduced by William Caslon IV in a circular dated Salisbury Square, 1 Jan, 1810.[22] The whereabouts of this document are not known.

How important this invention was technologically is shown by the following:

'. . . to him [Caslon] we owe the greatest improvement in the art of type-founding that has taken place in modern times; mainly the pierced matrices for large types which he, without impropriety, denominated Sans-pareil.' [21]

For an early description of this process, which is more detailed than the one in the *Caslon Circular* of July 1877, see page 39.

At a meeting in 1813 of the London Association of Master Letter Founders, Figgins protested that 'these types . . . from their cheapness [1s. 10d. per lb as offered by Caslon] will be so generally used as almost to exclude Large Letters cast in the usual manner.' The Society's decision was that the new method would 'not do the trade the injury apprehended.' As the Sanspareil matrix was not patented by Caslon it became a boon to his fellow typefounders, including Figgins, who quickly made use of it.

The Caslon type specimen book which is usually ascribed to the years 1816 shows types from fifteen to six lines Pica inclusive, labelled proudly 'Sanspareil'. This is paralleled by Figgins using the 'Cast in Moulds & Matrices' as an equivalent description for Sanspareil for exactly the same sizes. Incidentally, a contemporary hand has added to the Caslon fifteen lines Pica in the Blake & Garnett specimen of 1819 the same *Cast in Moulds and Matrices*. From five lines down ordinary matrices were used. The thinner lines in smaller types are easier to achieve 'in the usual manner' with a punch worked from outside than with a stencil worked from inside.

As to the design of the letters it is interesting to find that the capitals still show curved bracketing in their serifs, whilst the lower case has straight linear modern style serifs without any curvature.

The addition of a heavier version (No 2) to the eight lines Pica shows the trend towards ever bolder types. In our copy the heading for the ordinary version is still EIGHT LINES PICA which has been changed in the Oxford and Sheffield copies to EIGHT LINES PICA No 1. This shows that the former leaves were printed before the additional No 2 were cut.

Another variant is the change from *MAYN* (Eight lines Pica italic) to *MANY* in the Oxford and Sheffield specimens. By the way on this leaf we observe that the terminals of the downstrokes are hollowed. In the Oxford and Sheffield copies the seven lines

Grand State Lottery

BEGINS DRAWING

JUNE 28, 1808.

SCHEME.				THE
6	Prizes of £20,000	are	£120,000	**ONLY**
2	 10,000	....	20,000	*LOTTERY*
2	 5,000	....	10,000	
3	 2,000	....	6,000	THAT
5	 1,000	....	5,000	EVER CONTAINED
7	 500	....	3,500	
20	 100	....	2,000	**6**
30	 50	....	1,500	
1,000	 22	....	22,000	
4,000	 15	....	60,000	
25,000 Tickets.			£250,000	PRIZES OF
NO FIXED PRIZE.				**£20,000.**

Tickets and Shares are Selling by

SWIFT & Co.

11, Poultry; and 12, Charing-Cross.

Gye and Balne, Printers, 38, Gracechurch-Street.

Lottery bill, London 1808

Pica has a bolder version with straight triangular serifs added as No 2 together with a backward-leaning italic. The paper of the roman specimen in the Sheffield copy is watermarked 1817.

Similar bolder (No 2) additions have been made to the six lines Pica in the two other copies and again there the headings of the original 'six lines Pica' roman and italic have the 'No 1' added.

As already indicated only the very large sizes of type were cast in the labour-saving Sanspareil matrices. The types from Five lines Pica down were produced in the ordinary manner: first a punch was cut in relief with the image of the letter in reverse on its end; the matrix then was the result of striking this punch into a copper bar (see also page 37).

The large types were of course intended to be used mainly on posters, but we find them also being used on the covers of books of engravings. The displaying of names of towns in the specimens invites their use on coaching placards.

The '£20,000!' on the Five lines Pica No 1 specimen definitely connects it with lottery bills,[23] on many of which this desirable sum figured prominently.

There was even a song, 'Twenty Thousand, or Tom Truelove's Journal', that used it as refrain; I am quoting the fourth stanza:

> At one, I sought the gen'rous lass,
>> Who long for me and love had tarried,
> And told her what had come to pass;
>> At two, we settled to be married;
> At three, we bought the wedding-ring,
>> At four, resolved to take a house, and
> Till five, did nought but dance and sing,
>> For joy of getting *Twenty Thousand.*

I am inclined to believe that the five lines Pica Roman No 1 and No 2 with their outsize headings were cut before 1810. The Oxford and Sheffield copies have '123456789!' instead of the '£20,000!' In, about 1817 a movement was started against the lottery-mania, which may help to explain this alteration.

Five lines Pica, No 2, which is bolder in its lower case only, has Quousque ta/ndem abute-/ABCDEFGHI in the two other copies and no numerals at all. The bold five lines Pica italic has 'No 2'

23

added to its heading and the splendid five lines Pica, 'shaded' has been changed to 'in shade' elsewhere.

It is worth noting that the sizes given in the respective headings, down to four lines Pica inclusive, indicate only the height of capitals and also that of the ascending minuscule letters. This fact can easily be ascertained with the help of a type rule. The descending lower case letters however are cast on the same body. Altogether the apparent size of this type, by present-day standards, is therefore larger than specified in the headings. It also means that lines of these types can be set much closer, whenever descenders and ascenders do not happen to clash.

As an example, the letters 'Q' and 'q' on the so-called five and four line specimens show the use of kerning (see also page 38). Only these two series amongst the large sizes in the book show ascending as well as descending letters, and as they moreover, for good measure, give two lines of them, we can examine the unusual way of positioning the face of the type on its given body. This system saves metal and as types were sold by weight, it was more economical to the printer. A similar material-saving method is still used nowadays with poster type, cut on wood.

The two lines Great Primer roman and italic have their headings set in a generously large type in a style similar to the Five lines Pica No 1 and others. These headings were also reduced in size with the addition of 'No 1'. in the Oxford and Sheffield copies.

There are other variations even to the make-up of actual copy on several specimens, but it is impossible to list all of these.

On the page of the two lines English No 2 roman is a set of Arabic numerals, deleted elsewhere.

To recapitulate: a two lines English No 1 is absent from the 1815 specimen book. We are pleased however to be able to re-produce it on page 14, as it appeared as Figgin's first effort in 1792.

We notice a marked change in formation of serifs, from the old style, bracketed ones of the two lines English No 2 to the distinctly modern style of the capitals of the No 3 in the same series.

Great Primer No 2 and Double Pica No 2 are printed in an extended form, on a separate page each in the Oxford and Sheffield specimen books. I am reproducing here the upper half of one of these to show the only change in the roman of the Great Primer

Quousque tandem abutere, Catilina, patientia nostra? quamdiu nos etiam furor iste tuus eludet? quem ad finem sese effrenata jactabit audacia? nihilne te nocturnum præsidium palatii, nihil urbis vigiliæ, nihil timor populi, nihil consensus bonorum omnium, nihil hic munitissimus habendi senatus locus, nihil horum ora vultusque moverunt? patere tua consilia non sentis? constric tam jam omnium horum conscientia teneri conjurationem tuam non vides?

ABCDEFGHIJKLMNOPQRS

☞ £ 1234567890

Variant from the [1817] specimen

No 2: a capital 'Q' in modern style, instead of the one, still in the Baskerville tradition, in our first edition of 1815.

I leave it to the reader to discover for himself the minutiae of subtle change of weight and variation of form in the smaller sizes of type even within the different numbers of one series.

The question marks for instance, particularly in the italic, are of considerable diversity of style. On the other hand the same capitals were used for the roman of English No 4, No 5 and No 6, to point to one curious fact out of many.

One of the earliest types in the book is the Brevier No 1, the punches of which were also used to produce Minion No 1. Both sizes of type share also the two sets of numerals, one of old style (non-ranging) and the other of modern style (ranging) figures.

The smallest type, shown in two-column setting, is Diamond, also used on the title page within the composite border.

The two line No 2 letters (Titling), which cover two pages in the model for our facsimile, have in the other copies a heading in larger type; three sizes of type on the first page and an addition of three smaller sizes on the second page. Comparison within the books shows that for these titling letters use has been made of the following sets of punches:

Capitals of French Canon No 2 for two line Great Primer No 2
Capitals of two lines Great Primer No 2 for two line Pica
Capitals of two lines Pica for two line Long Primer.

The business of managing a type foundry then was complex (see also pages 36-41) and the master letterfounder had to see to it that the activities in all the branches of the work were properly co-ordinated. In some case he may have been capable of cutting punches himself; as was the case with William Caslon I and II, with Thomas Cottrell and with Joseph Jackson. I do not doubt that Figgins belonged to those few, who had acquired that skill. But it is also known that he had great difficulties in finding the punch cutter, when early in his career he was asked to supply some Greek founts to the Oxford Press. Who were the artists or 'clever mechanics', as they were described at the time ? We cannot even be quite certain whether the founder employed punch cutters on the premises of the foundry; some of them probably had their own workshops. One of the most active engravers of this kind was Richard Austin[24], who cut the famous series of types for John Bell. He may well have cut other types for Figgins, apart from the one which has been authenticated and which appears on the 1801 specimen (see page 17).

I was delighted to discover some contemporary notes, pencilled on some of the pages in the Sheffield copy, which help us to assign certain of the types; some to a certain Perry, and some to one Edmonston. Moreover, on the flyleaf[25] their names and addresses appear, hardly legible, but with some difficulty one can just manage to reconstruct and read:

Perry No 6 Britannia Place/Battle Bridge
Edmonston Alfred/Place Cambridge Heath

On the lower margin of the title page in this Sheffield copy we find written in two lines, in pencil and difficult to read:

Perry cut these/cut the small Flower

A catalogue from the year 1846 of an auction, which never took place, of the Caslon Foundry lists not only the punches and matrices but also mentions the names of their punch cutters. It is therefore an important source for checking. A Perry is mentioned once as having supplied matrices of a Canon roman No 2 and a certain Edmiston who is mentioned fourteen times is, I assume, our Edmonston. He collaborated in three of the types with Boileau, and once with Bessemer. Edmiston's types in the Caslon list range from English Antique [Egyptian] to Diamond roman. This is interesting as it tallies more or less with the pencil notes in the Sheffield copy, as we see on the following specimens:

On Pica No 7	*Edmonston has cut a new Pica No 6*
	. . . a thin & strong . . .
On Long Primer No 1	
(not in 1815 copy)	*Edmonston*
On Long Primer No 6	*Edmonston*
On Brevier No 6	
(not in 1815 copy)	*Edmonston*
On Diamond	*Edmonston*
	Edmonston has cut a new Nonpareil

The Caslon auction catalogue connects Edmiston (alias Edmonston) with a Nonpareil italic, (Bessemer & Edmiston) ditto roman; Pearl roman (Edmiston & Boileau); Brevier italic; Diamond roman, etc. He seems to have specialised in the smaller sizes of type.

If we can trust these contemporary pencil notes we are able then to ascribe certain specimens in the Figgins's book to Perry and Edmiston. I have tried on the basis of their addresses to consult the rate books of the time. Battle Bridge, St Pancras, was at the North end of Gray's-Inn-Lane, 'near a mile from Holborn, and W. end of Pentonville',[26] where King's Cross is now. The Camden Borough Librarian informs me that no Perry can be traced in the records.

Cambridge-Heath, Hackney Road, is '1⅛ of a mile from Shoreditch-church, by the turnpike towards Hackney'.[26] The record office at County Hall states that the rate books of Bethnal

Green from 1775-1911 were sent for salvage during the war. I regret to say that a search in the directories of the period was equally disappointing.

Anybody who has cut a letter punch appreciates the great effort that must have gone into preparing whole ranges of various types as they appear in the specimen book of Vincent Figgins. It is therefore not without importance to be able to consult contemporary writing, as to the time required to produce one fount of type.

A report of the [Royal] Society of Arts from the year 1818[27] has this to say about the punch-cutter:

'This is the most difficult and confined art; not more than four or five artists could be found in this kingdom capable of cutting the punches for a Diamond type . . . The works of one artist in this line are as well known from those of another, as in plate engraving. I [T. C. Hansard] know of but three sets of Diamond punches in England; each is distinguishable by a common eye, and by the profession known by whom cut, or rather cast; as the letter-founder is, invariably, the employer of the punch-cutter. The number of punches necessary to complete a *fount*, or every sort used, is very great . . . An artist of the greatest industry could not cut more than two in a day. After they are completed for the ordinary number . . . it will take a founder six months in matrix-making, justifying, mould making, casting, dressing, &c. before he could deliver any thing complete for printing; but it should be remarked, that these materials being once perfected, are of ever-lasting duration.'

The report then continues to describe the letter-founder's department:

'The *Justifier* also strikes the matrices into copper, by the punches. This is no part of the punch-cutter's art, it is confined to the founder himself, or his manager.

The *Mould-maker*, also a separate branch of the founder's business.

The *Caster*—a separate department in the foundery, even the best of whom (and none but the choicest caster can be employed on Diamond, or small type) is incapable of the other departments.

Breaker-off, Rubber, Kerner, Setter-up, Dresser; all various and separate departments in a foundery, no two of which are ever united in the same hand.'

Further on in the same document we find a statement from a letter by Anthony Bessemer, the punch-cutter:

'That the time required to engrave a diamond lower case alphabet and doubles, consisting of 33 punches, would be about 6 weeks; and that the same time would be required for a set of capitals of 28 punches.'

Mr. Caslon, the letter-founder, in his turn stated:

'That the punches of the diamond type cast by him were cut by Mr. Bessemer, and that for this fount of type at least 150 punches must have been cut, as every separate letter and character requires a separate punch. He thinks that it would be scarcely possible for one person to complete a fount of letters from first to last. In the ordinary course of business the mere preparation of the types after the punch-cutter has finished his process, goes through the following eight different hands; 1st, the justifier, who strikes the matrices; 2nd, the mould maker; 3rd, the caster; 4th, the breaker off; 5th, the rubber; 6th, the kerner; 7th, the setter up; 8th, the dresser. Two of these are boys; and although the work might no doubt be executed by fewer than eight different hands (this particular number being however adopted as most conducive to expedition and excellence of work); yet that the whole could be gone through by one person he thinks barely and scarcely possible, he has himself never heard of an instance of such having been the case. If only one person was employed in each department, a fount of types could scarcely be completed in 7 or 8 months; at present there are only 4 or 5 persons in England who can execute diamond type, owing no doubt to the limited demand for it; and the peculiar style of each of these punch cutters is perfectly well known to persons conversant with letter founding . . .

It would take a person a day to cut two punches of diamond type, and in his opinion Mr. Bessemer could not get ready for the founder a complete fount of diamond type in less than 4 or 5 months; and to get the types from the punches ready for use would occupy 6 or 8 months longer.'

(For further documentation and illustration see pages 36-41).

It is intriguing to find in the Caslon Sale Catalogue (see above) the names of Bessemer and Edmiston linked with the production of one type face. As we see from the report, Bessemer was the expert who cut a Diamond type for Caslon. From the pencil notes we found that Edmonston did the same for the foundry of Figgins. We have established now the names of three punch-cutters who supplied him with punches or matrices: Austin, Perry and Edmiston. Who the mysterious 'Black Man', the engraver of the Greek commissioned by Oxford, was, we may never be able to find out.[28]

Even if Vincent Figgins employed or commissioned other punch-cutters to produce the types, his was the controlling spirit; and it was his diligence which enabled him to build up so impressive a foundry from exiguous beginnings. It was his sound taste, nurtured by eighteenth-century traditions, but accepting also the new trends, which justified such eulogies as Hansard's: 'Mr Figgins, in all the reputation he could desire, . . . has never . . . ceased in his efforts to make his foundry one of the most complete in England. No foundry is better stocked with matrices for those extraneous sorts which are cut more with a view to accommodation than profit, . . . and I feel it particularly incumbent on me to add that, as his specimen bears equal rank with any for the number and beauty of its founts; so he has strayed less into the folly of fat-faced, preposterous, disproportion, than either Thorne, Fry, or Caslon.'

I have not hesitated in my consideration of certain aspects of type production at the turn of the eighteenth to the nineteenth century to include voices, mainly contemporary, that were critical of the then modern trends; they helped to underline the axiom that anything new in human development will soon enough find its violent antagonists, reasonable or otherwise.

In retrospect we can see more clearly the causes of certain changes in typographical style. We may agree sometimes with the critics and sometimes with the criticised. But without the efforts of the latter the typographical scene would not have been enriched. It is a fact that many of the types Vincent Figgins produced and propagated are still with us as useful tools of communication, even though many of the matrices seem to have perished recently; and in bringing out this book in 1967 we endeavour to honour him by marking the 175th anniversary of the beginning of his own type foundry.

NOTES

1 Wolffgang Fugger's *Handwriting Manual* etc., 1553. Translated by Frederick Plaat. Foreword by Harry Carter, O.U.P., 1960.
2 André Jammes, *Académisme et Typographie*, The Making of the *Romain du Roi*. Journal of the Printing Historical Society, I. 1965.
3 George Cumberland (c. 1760-1848); painter, engraver and author. Friend of William Blake, who engraved most of the *Outlines*.
4 Gabriel Giolito de Ferrari, a Venetian sixteenth century printer.
5 George Cumberland, *Thoughts on Outline, Sculpture* etc: Accompanied with free remarks on the practice of the moderns, and liberal hints cordially intended for their advantage. London, 1796.
6 The famous entirely engraved edition of *Horace* produced by John Pine in London between 1733 and 1737.
7 A translation of the Reports of Berlier & Sobry etc. edited with an introduction by Daniel Berkeley Updike. *The Fleuron:* A Journal of Typography, VI, edited by Stanley Morison. Cambridge, 1928.
8 John McCreery, *The Press;* a poem. Published as a specimen of typography. Liverpool, 1803.
9 B. Wolpe, 'Caslon Architectural. On the origin and design of the large letters cut and cast by William Caslon II'. *Alphabet*. London, 1964.
10 See also James Mosley, 'English Vernacular', *Motif* 11, 1963.
11 Talbot Baines Reed, *The History of the Old English Letter Foundries*. Edited by A. F. Johnson. London, 1952. James Mosley, 'The Type Foundry of Vincent Figgins 1792 - 1836'. *Motif* 1, Nov. 1958.
12 That it was not unusual for a type founder to produce a specimen of a single size of a new type together with a title leaf is shown in John Bell's English roman (1788), cut by Richard Austin. See Stanley Morison, *John Bell*, 1745-1831. Cambridge, 1930.
13 Reproduced from the only known copy, in the author's collection.
14 Joseph Ames in his *Typographical Antiquities* in 1749 was the first to discard the long s. But this was only an isolated event. John Bell was the first to introduce this typographic novelty in most of his publications from 1785 on. Leigh Hunt in his autobiography has a note about this: 'An intelligent compositor (Mr J. P. S. Bicknell), who has been a noter of curious passages in his time, informs me that Bell was the first printer who confined the small letter s to its present shape, that this innovation, besides the handsomer form of the new letter, was "a boon to master-printers and the compositor, inasmuch as it lessened the amount of capital necessary to be laid out under the old system, and saved to the workman no small portion of his valuable time and labour." '
15 In author's collection (only known copy). Paper size of original $18\frac{7}{8}$ x $13\frac{1}{2}$. Watermark: WHATMAN 1794.
16 The open types reappear in the speciments of the mid 1830s and were re-issued in the present century as 'Gresham'.

17 For an outrageous counterblast to this praise see the opinions of William Morris and Emery Walker in their article 'Printing' in *Arts and Crafts Essays*. London, 1893:
      'It was reserved for the founders of the later eighteenth century to produce letters which are *positively* ugly, and which, it may be added, are dazzling and unpleasant to the eye owing to the clumsy thickening and vulgar thinning of the lines. . . . The Italian, Bodoni and the Frenchman, Didot, were the leaders in this luckless change, though our own Baskerville, who was at work some years before them, went much on the same lines; but his letters, though uninteresting, are not nearly so gross and vulgar as those of either the Italian or the Frenchman.'

18 The Oxford copy has 120 leaves, two of which are watermarked 1817, whereas the Sheffield copy has 125, six of which are watermarked 1817, my own 76. The Sheffield copy although dated 1815 on the title has 1820 on the original typographic binding.

19 In comparison, the specimen books of Caslon in the 1760s and later were printed on foldable sheets in the orthodox manner and bound in the normal way. Therefore they can easily be described bibliographically, while each copy of this Figgins specimen book has variant problems.

20 The single leaves of the whole book are knocked together and trimmed at the back. The trimmed surface is then provisionally covered with glue. When this has set the bulk of leaves is broken up into sections of about a dozen, which are the artificial equivalent of folded sections. These can be oversewn with thread about $\frac{1}{8}''$ distance from the glued surface. Afterwards the sections are sewn in the usual fashion.

21 Thomas Curson Hansard, *Typographia* etc. London, 1825.

22 Reed, op. cit.

23 John Ashton, *A History of English Lotteries*. London, 1893.

24 In Austin's introduction to the specimen book of the *Austin's Imperial Letter Foundry* (c. 1819) he admonishes: 'Surely if founders had been their own punch cutters they would have foreseen the disadvantages of such a false style of cutting.'

25 On the same endpaper can be found written in ink in a clear hand the following: *Mr Carrol | York | With V Figgins Compl.*
      Prices the same as the Scotch Founders.
      At the time the Sheffield and Scottish typefounders tried to undercut the London ones and Figgins tried to reassure the York master printer that he could compete with the North Britons.

26 *Lockie's Topography of London*, etc. London, 1810.

27 Report of the Committee of the Society, &c. relative to the Mode of Preventing the Forgery of Banknotes. London, published 1819.

82 See James Figgins's story in Reed, op. cit.

APPENDICES

I

SIZES OF TYPE

Comparative table giving the traditional names of type sizes shown in the facsimile, and their modern approximate equivalents in points:

16 lines Pica	192pt	2 lines Pica	24pt
13 lines Pica	156pt	Double Pica	22pt
11 lines Pica	132pt	Great Primer	18pt
10 lines Pica	120pt	English	14pt
9 lines Pica	108pt	Pica	12pt
8 lines Pica	96pt	Small Pica	11pt
7 lines Pica	84pt	Long Primer	10pt
6 lines Pica	72pt	Bourgeois	9pt
5 lines Pica	60pt	Brevier	8pt
4 lines Pica	48pt	Minion	7pt
French Canon	48pt	Nonpareil	6pt
2 lines Great Primer	36pt	Pearl	5pt
2 lines English	28pt	Diamond	$4\frac{1}{2}$pt

DESCRIPTION OF THE TYPE FOUNDRY

The operations connected with a type foundery may be enumerated generally as follows:—1. Preparing the mould; 2. cutting the punches; 3. striking the matrix; 4. mixing and melting the metal; 5. casting; and 6. dressing the letters. The mould is a very ingenious, and somewhat complex contrivance: the two portions or halves, between which the types are actually cast, are of iron; but they are respectively attached to wooden backs, which render the whole convenient to hold, and at the same time prevent the hands from coming into contact with the metallic portions of the mould, which get heated during the progress of casting. The mould, as already stated, consists of two parts.

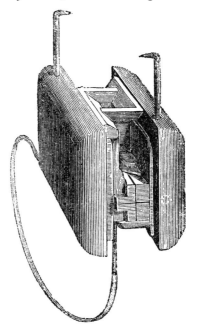

These two parts are so exactly fitted to each other, that, when properly placed together, a square funnel-shaped opening or mouth is formed for the more easy introduction of the melted metal, which a space remains open down the middle, adapted to the form and size of the intended letter. Two projecting knobs adapted to corresponding grooves, and called gauges, allow the two halves of the mould to slide sideward a trifle, as the shank of the letter may be required greater or less; or, in other words, to suit all letters of the same fount, from an *i* to an *m*.

The utmost attention and skill are required to ensure perfect accuracy in the fitting of every part of the mould, and particularly that the letters may come out exactly square, and the faces stand at perfectly right angles with the sides; without which they would neither admit of being composed for use without starting when wedged together in pages, nor would they form, *en masse*, that absolutely even surface, so essential in good printing. The securing of these ends is called justifying the mould; and during the operation, a number of trial letters are cast, and examined by a variety of delicate measurements, until their perfect accuracy is ascertained.

The next business is to prepare the matrix, or that part from which the figure or letter on the end of each type is immediately derived, and upon the perfection of which, therefore, the beauty or otherwise of the letter exclusively depends. The original of every letter is a steel punch, the execution of the figured end of which requires peculiar delicacy in the application of the various small files, punches, and gravers employed. The form of the letter is, in the first place, delineated either with a pen and ink, or, when very minute, with the point of a needle; the interstices being afterwards cut out*, and the outer parts filed away, leaving only the character itself in relief on the steel. Great nicety is required to develop the letter properly and with exact symmetry of all its parts, so as that the removal of the superfluous metal should not be too inconsiderable or overmuch: if the latter, the type will not wear well; if the former, it will not print clearly, but give a blurred impression.

When the punch is cut, tempered, and found perfect, the next thing done is to strike the matrix. The matrix is a piece of copper, about an inch and a half long, and of a breadth proportionate to the size of the letter it is intended to receive.

The steel punch is carefully struck to a proper depth into the copper near the end, and thus forms the matrix, which is afterwards filed; the surface being levelled, the bulging from the operation of the punch corrected, and cross nicks cut near the end farthest from the impression, which is afterwards slightly rounded. The mould and matrix being thus prepared, they are ready for the caster.

The metal used by the type founder is a composition consisting chiefly of lead and regulus of antimony, with a little tin, and sometimes other ingredients. The chief object of mixture is to obtain perfect fluidity, so that the counterpart of the matrix shall come away sharp and perfect; moreover, that the letters shall be hard enough to wear well, and stand to their work firmly, without at the same time becoming brittle: a type, however, will break sooner than bend. The ingredients and mixture of the metal differ in different establishments, and are generally kept secret; the stock meltings take place at certain seasons, under the inspection of the principal, when the metal is run into small ingots, and

*or struck in with a counter-punch (B.W.)

37

afterwards served out to the workmen as they may want it. It is melted for use in a small cast-iron pot, set in brick-work at a convenient height, and the fire so enclosed, that the workman is as little as possible annoyed by the heat and fumes. The number of these furnaces varies according to the extent of the establishment.

In proceeding to cast, the workman takes the two parts of the mould, and placing them together, an interior space is left up the middle of the mould, corresponding to the cubical body of the letter, and also answering exactly to the impression on the matrix, which is inserted in a nick and kept steadily in its place by the end of the spring, being brought to the groove in the outside of the matrix, and pressing against it. Holding the mould firmly in his left hand, he takes from the iron pot, by means of a small ladle in his right hand, as much metal as will suffice to cast the letter, and, besides that, nearly to fill the throat or funnel. The instant the workman has poured the metal into the mould, he gives it a peculiar jerk or heave upwards, in order to expel in some degree the air, and drive the metal fully into the matrix.

By removing the spring, the matrix is just drawn from the letter, which, on separating the parts of the mould, is thrown out to the heap on the work-bench. A single workman will cast 2000 or 3000 letters in a day.

In this state, each letter has a taper piece of metal or castable attached, which has been formed in the throat of the mould: these are carefully broken off by boys, after which the letters are ready for the further dressing. A boy, having his fore-finger defended by a little cap of leather, takes up the types one by one, and with singular rapidity rubs them on both sides upon a stone or smooth flat file laid on the board: they are then placed side by side in long sticks or rulers, which on being firmly screwed together, the types form a solid series, and are easily smoothed on their edges, by passing over them a scraping tool similar in form to a razor blade. In these dressing sticks they are likewise bearded and grooved, as the operations are called: the first consists in shaving away a small portion of the shoulder of each letter next the face, and the other in cutting a small semicircular groove in the foot; both these removals of superfluous metal are effected by passing a light iron plane with great address along the line of types, while they are wedged in a line between two parallel pieces of wood. A small semicircular groove, similar to that planed in the foot, is cast in one edge of the letter, by means of the projection of the wire in the mould. In some founts of letters there are two or three of these nicks: they form a continued gutter along the outside of a line of letters while in the composing-stick, and when none of them are in an inverted position.

There are some sorts, called kerned letters, in which a small portion of one type extends over the corner of another, as the tail of the italic j, and the beak of the f: these require greater care in the dressing. To obviate one difficulty in the joining of letters of this sort, between which, on account of their inclination, or bending parts, the space would be considerable, some of them are cast together, as *ff, fi, fl*. In some cases, the small roman f has been cast with the upper part a little bent backward, to allow of its setting up in the regular way.

Besides the letters themselves, points, figures, spaces, quadrats, &c. are cast of sizes to correspond; a complete series of these being called a fount.

The very large letters, impressions from which we frequently see in placards, were formerly called sand letters, from their having originally been moulded and cast in sand. A method, however, of casting them in metal moulds in a similar manner to that which is practised with the smaller sorts, was devised by the late Mr W. Caslon, and is now adopted in all type founderies. The matrices for these large characters are not made by striking with punches, as above described, but by cutting the design of the letter quite through a piece of brass [stencil like] about a quarter of an inch thick, and then closely rivetting it upon a back plate of the same metal. The mould also, instead of being held in the hand while the metal is poured in, is attached to two iron rods, and placed during the casting over brackets on the work-bench.

Extracts from Dionysius Lardner, *The Cabinet Cyclopaedia*, London, 1834.

Note to illustrations:
The wood engraving of the casting mould on page 36 is an enlargement from *The Penny Magazine*, London, 1833. From the same source comes the engraving on page 40. This is also enlarged and somewhat trimmed at the top.

III

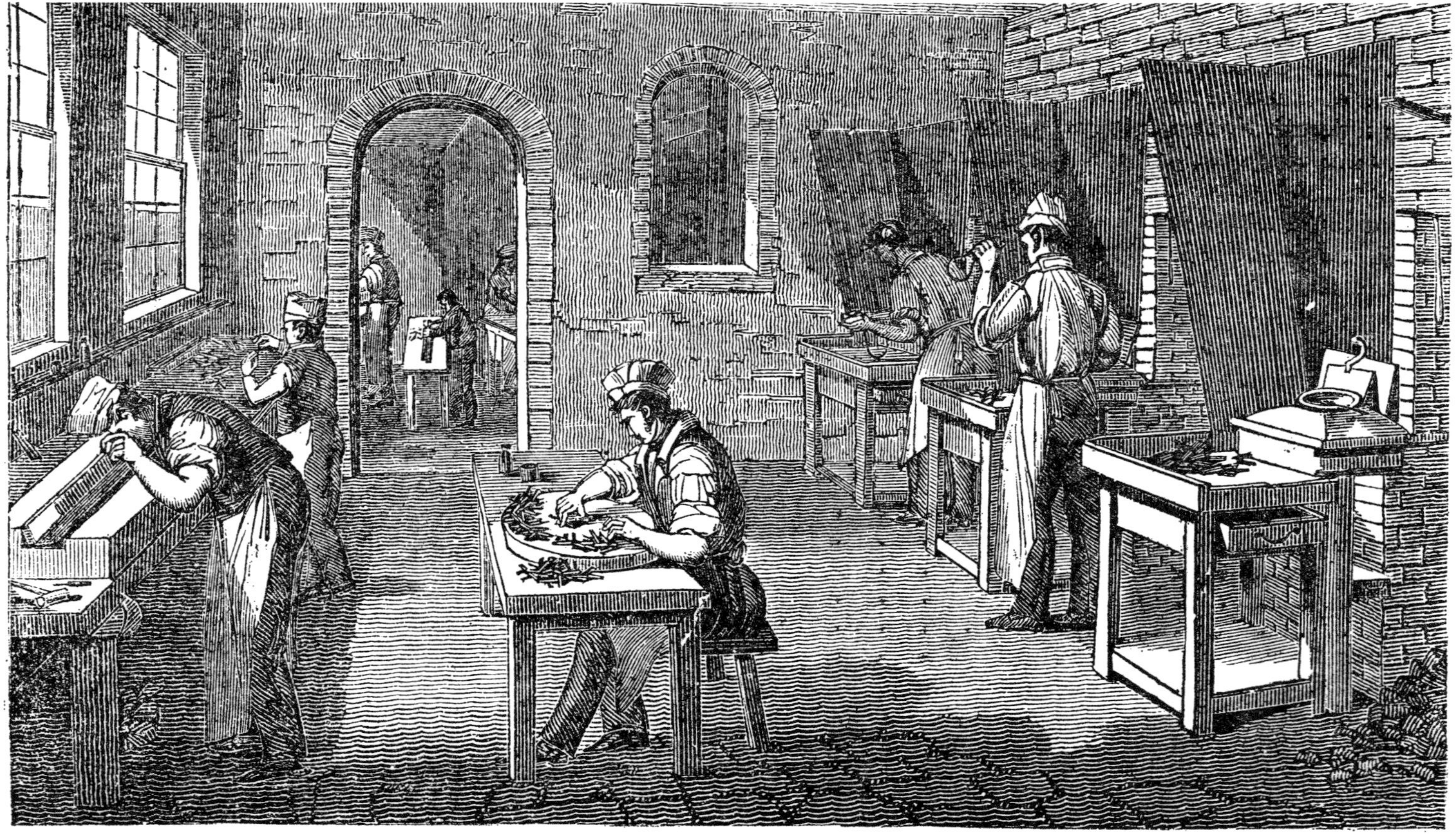

In the large cut there is a representation of three furnaces. At the first, which is unoccupied, may be seen the little table at which the founder works, and the pot out of which he dips the heated metal with a very small ladle. At the second furnace the workman is shown at the moment after he has poured the metal into the mould. And at the third, the other workman is represented in the act of separating the two parts of the mould, and picking out the letter from the lower half, with the hook shown at the top edge of the other half.

From the table of the caster the heap of types cast is from time to time removed by a boy to another table. It is his business to break off the superfluous metal; and this he does with such rapidity that the mode in which he operates can scarcely be followed by the eye. Some boys have been known to break off 5000 in an hour; the average number is 2000. This rapidity is the more remarkable, as the boy must seize the type, not upon the flat surface, but upon its edges, or he would otherwise break or bend it.

From the *breaking-off boy* the types are removed to the *rubber*. In the wood-cut this workman is represented seated in the centre. A round grit-stone is before him, upon which is a heap of types. The fore and middle fingers of his right hand are armed with a piece of tarred leather; and he passes each side (not the edges) of the type smartly over the stone, turning it, of course, in the movement. This, again, is an example of wonderful rapidity; 2000 types are thus rubbed in an hour.

From the rubber the heap is conveyed to a boy whose business is to set up the types in lines, in a long shallow frame. The face of each must be uppermost, and the nicks outward. The rate at which this boy works is the same as the rubber.

When the types are once set up in lines, they are never again deranged till they are given out to be used by the printer. The long frame, filled with a single line of type, is removed to the *dresser*. By the application of other frames, he is enabled to dress, or polish them, on each edge; and, turning them with the face downwards, to channel-cut with a plane a groove in the bottom, so that they will stand steadily. It will be at once understood how necessary it is that every letter should be perfectly square and true, when it is considered that if they were not of uniform height the impression could not be even.

Each letter being tied up in lines of convenient length, the proportionate numbers of each variety, small letters, points, capitals, small capitals, and figures, are selected; and the fount is ready for delivery to the printer.

Extracts from *The Penny Magazine*, London, 1833

41

ACKNOWLEDGEMENTS

It is my pleasant duty to thank Mr Harry Carter, the archivist of The University Press, Oxford, for allowing me to examine the library's Figgins specimen book; Mr James Blake of Stephenson Blake, type-founders of Sheffield, for making their copy available to me, a kindness which enabled me to find new information about punch cutters of the period.

I am grateful to Mrs E. M. Hatt and to my daughter Sarah for reading the manuscript; to Mrs Joan Newman for typing it; to Mr Iain Bain, to Mr Christopher Bradshaw and to Mr James Mosley, the Librarian of St Bride's Printing Library, for reading the proofs and for making valuable suggestions.

Also I am greatly obliged to the librarian and staff of the following libraries: Camden Borough Central Library; Guildhall Library; London University Library; St Bride's Library; the Typographical Library at the University Press, Oxford.

Finally the Society is very grateful to Mr Bernard Roberts for the care he and his press have taken in printing this book.

ENVOI

The largest and the longest kind
    Possess the foremost page,
A sort most needed by the blind,
    Or nearly such from age.

The full-charged leaf, which next ensues,
    Presents in bright array
The smaller sort, which matrons use,
    Not quite so blind as they.

The third, the fourth, the fifth supply
    What their occasions ask,
Who, with a more discerning eye,
    Perform a nicer task.

But still with regular decrease,
    From size to size they fall,
In every leaf grows less and less;
    The last are least of all.

O! what a fund of genius, pent
    In narrow space, is here!
This volume's method and intent
    How luminous and clear.

It leaves no reader at a loss,
    Or posed, whoever reads;
No commentator's tedious gloss,
    Nor even index needs.

William Cowper

The stanzas on the preceding page are from Cowper's riddling poem, 'A Manual' (presumably about a book of needles; but was it a type specimen book which the poet had also in mind?)

FACSIMILE

---

of the 1815 Specimen Book

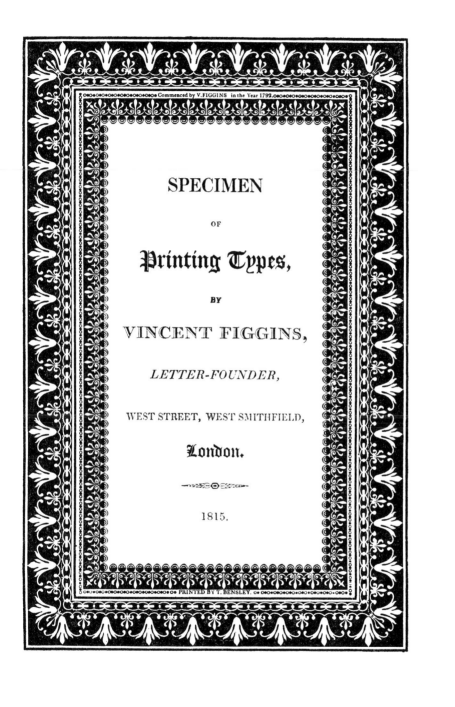

Commenced by V. FIGGINS in the Year 1792.

SPECIMEN

OF

𝕻rinting 𝕿ypes,

BY

VINCENT FIGGINS,

LETTER-FOUNDER,

WEST STREET, WEST SMITHFIELD,

London.

1815.

PRINTED BY T. BENSLEY.

13 Lines Pica. Cast in Mould & Matrixes.

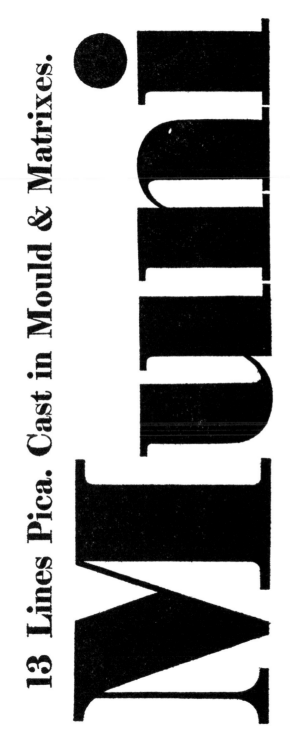

Mull

V. FIGGINS.

13 Lines Pica. Cast in Mould & Matrixes.

Moon

V. FIGGINS.

Eleven Lines Pica. Cast in Mould & Matrixes.

MINE

mane

V. FIGGINS.

Eleven Lines Pica. Cast in Mould & Matrixes.

MIVE

mowe

V. FIGGINS.

Ten Lines Pica. Cast in Mould & Matrixes.

MINE
maline

V. FIGGINS.

Ten Lines Pica. Cast in Mould & Matrixes.

MINE.

Moone

V. FIGGINS.

Nine Lines Pica, Cast in Mould & Matrixes.

MEND.

maitre

V Figgins.

MINE moone

Nine Lines Pica, Cast in Mould & Matrixes.

V. FIGGINS.

EIGHT LINES PICA. Cast in Mould & Matrixes.

MINOR
mineral

V.Figgins.

EIGHT LINES PICA. Cast in Mould & Matrixes.

HUME

mentor

V.FIGGINS.

EIGHT LINES PICA, No. 2. CAST IN MOULD & MATRIXES.

MAINE

miltons

MAYTON

mentor

V. Figgins.

SEVEN LINES PICA.   Cast in Mould & Matrixes.

MYRTLE

munster

V. FIGGINS.

SEVEN LINES PICA.   Cast in Mould & Matrixes.

MINTO!

number

V. FIGGINS.

MILTON,

Burnham.

1234567890

V. FIGGINS.

—

SIX LINES PICA. *Cast in Mould & Matrixes.*

HOMER
munition

V.FIGGINS.

FIVE LINES PICA, No. 1.

DURHAM.

Chelmsford,

£20,000!

V. FIGGINS.

FIVE LINES PICA, No. 2.

Maidstone,

BINGLEY.

1234567890

v. FIGGINS.

FIVE LINES PICA.

Quousque ta
ndem abuter
ABCDEFG

V. FIGGINS.

Five Lines Pica, No. 3.

Quousque ta
ndem abute-

ABCDEFGT

v. FIGGINS.

FIVE LINES PICA, SHADED.

ABCDEFGH
IJKLMNOP
RSTUVWX.

V. FIGGINS.

Quousque tand-
em abutere, Cat
ABCDEFGHM
£1234567890

V. FIGGINS.

Quousque tandem
abutere Catilina
patientia nostra,
ABCDEFGM.

V. FIGGINS.

Quousque tandem abute
re, Catilina, patientia nos
tra? quamdiu nos etiam.
ABCDEFGHIJKLMN
1234567890

V. FIGGINS.

FRENCH CANON, No. 1.

Quousque tandem abute-
re, Catilina, patientia no
stra? quamdiu nos etiam
furor iste tuus eludet? li
ABCDEFGHIJKLM

V.FIGGINS.

French Canon, No. 2.

Quousque tandem abutere, Catilina, patientia nostra? quamdiu nos et

ABCDEFGHIJKLM?

£1234567890.

V. FIGGINS.

Quousque tandem abu-
tere, Catilina, patientia
nostra? quamdiu nos e-
tiam furor iste tuus elu

ABCDEFGHIJKLM

V. FIGGINS.

Two Lines Great Primer.

Quousque tandem abutere, Catilina, patientia nostra? quamdiu nos etiam furor iste tuus el
udet? quem ad finem sese effrenata jactabit audacia? nihilne te

ABCDEFGHIJKLMNOPQ
1234567890

v. FIGGINS.

Two Lines Great Primer.

Quousque tandem abutere, Catilina, patientia nostra? quamdiu nos etiam furor iste tuus el
udet? quem ad finem sese effrenata jactabit audacia, nihilne te

ABCDEFGHIJKLMNOP

V. FIGGINS.

Two Lines Great Primer, No. 2.

Quousque tandem abutere, Ca
tilina, patientia nostra? quam
diu nos etiam furor iste tuus e
ludet? quem ad finem sese effrenata jactabit audacia? nihi
ABCDEFGHIJKLMNOPQ
£1234567890.

V.FIGGINS.

Two Lines Great Primer, No. 2.

Quousque tandem abutere, Catilina, patientia nostra? quamdiu nos
etiam furor iste tuus eludet? quem
ad finem sese effrenata jactabit au
dacia, nihilne te nocturnum præsi
ABCDEFGHIJKLMNOPRS

V. FIGGINS.

Two Lines English, No.2.

Quousque tandem abutere, Catilina, patientia nostra? quamdiu nos etiam furor
iste tuus eludet? quem ad finem sese effrenata jactabit audacia? nihilne te nocturnum præsidium palatii, nihil urbis vi-
giliae, nihil timor populi, nihil consensus
ABCDEFGHIJKLMNOPQRSTUV
1234567890

V. FIGGINS.

Two Lines English, No.2.

Quousque tandem abutere, Catilina, patientia nostra? quamdiu nos etiam furor
iste tuus eludet? quem ad finem sese effrenata jactabit audacia? nihilne te nocturnum praesidium palatii, nihil urbis vi-
giliae, nihil timor populi, nihil consensus
ABCDEFGHIJKLMNOPQRST

V. FIGGINS.

Two Lines English, No.3.

Quousque tandem abutere, Catilina, patientia nostra? quamdiu nos etiam furor iste tuus eludet? quem ad finem sese effrenata jactabit audacia? nihilne te nocturnum præsidium palatii, nihil urbis vigiliæ nihil timor populi, nihil consensus bonoru

ABCDEFGHIJKLMNOPQRSTUVX
1234567890

V. FIGGINS.

Two Lines English, No.3.

Quousque tandem abutere, Catilina, patientia nostra? quamdiu nos etiam furor
iste tuus eludet? quem ad finem sese effrenata jactabit audacia? nihilne te nocturnum præsidium palatii, nihil urbis vigiliæ, nihil timor populi, nihil consensus
ABCDEFGHIJKLMNOPQRSTUV

V. FIGGINS.

Two Lines Pica.

Quousque tandem abutere, Catilina, patientia nostra? quamdiu nos etiam furor iste tuus eludet? quem ad finem sese effrenata jactabit audacia? nihilne te nocturnum præsidium palatii nihil urbis vigiliæ, nihil timor populi, nihil con sensus bonorum omnium nihil hic munitissimu habendi senatus locus, nihil horum ora vultus-

ABCDEFGHIJKLMNOPQRSTUVW.
£1234567890.

V.FIGGINS.

Two Lines Pica.

Quousque tandem abutere, Catilina, patientia nostra? quamdiu nos etiam furor iste tuus eludet? quem ad finem sese effrenata jactabit audacia? nihilne te nocturnum præsidium palatii, nihil urbis vigiliæ nihil timor populi, nihil consensus bonorum omnium, nihil hic munitissimus habendi senatus locus, nihil horum ora vultusque.

ABCDEFGHIJKLMNOPQRSTUVD

V. FIGGINS.

Quousque tandem abutere, Catilina,
patientia nostra? quamdiu nos etiam
furor iste tuus eludet? quem ad finem
sese effrenata jactabit audacia? Nihil
ne te nocturnum præsidium palatii, ni
ABCDEFGHIJKLMNOPQRS

*Quousque tandem abutere, Catilina, pa
tientia nostra? quamdiu nos etiam furor iste tuus eludet? quem ad finem se
se effrenata jactabit audacia? Nihilne
te nocturnum præsidium palatii, nihil
ABCDEFGHIJKLMNOPQR*

Quousque tandem abutere, Ca
tilina, patientia nostra? quamdiu nos etiam, furor iste tuus
eludet? quem ad finem sese ef
ABCDEFGHIJKLMNOP

*Quousque tandem abutere, Cati
lina, patientia nostra? quamdiu
nos etiam furor iste tuus eludet
quem ad finem sese effrenata ja
ABCDEFGHIJKLMNO*

V.FIGGINS.

DOUBLE PICA, No. 3.
Quousque tandem abutere, Ca
tilina, patientia nostra? quam
diu nos etiam furor iste tuus
eludet? quem ad finem sese ef
frenata jactabit audacia? nihil
ne te nocturnum præsidium pa
latii, nihil urbis vigiliæ, nihil ti
mor populi, nihil consensus bo
norum omnium, nihil hic muni
tissimus habendi senatus locus
ABCDEFGHIJKLMNOP
£1234567890.
*Quousque tandem abutere, Cati
lina, patientia nostra? quamdiu
nos etiam furor iste tuus eludet
quem ad finem sese effrenata jac
tabit audacia? nihilne te noctur
num præsidium palatii, nihil urbis vigiliæ, nihil timor populi, ni
hil consensus bonorum omnium,
nihil hic munitissimus habendi se
natus locus, nihil horum ora vul-
ABCDEFGHIJKLMNO.*

V. FIGGINS.

Great Primer, No. 3.

Quousque tandem abutere, Catilina, patientia nostra? quamdiu nos etiam furor iste tuus eludet? quem ad finem sese effrenata jactabit audacia? nihilne te nocturnum præsidium palatii, ni hil urbis vigiliæ, nihil timor populi, ni hil consensus bonorum omnium, nihil hic munitissimus habendi senatus locus, nihil horum ora vultusque moverunt? patere tua consilia non sentis? constrictam jam omnium horum cons

ABCDEFGHIJKLMNOPQR
£1234567890.

Quousque·tandem abutere, Catilina, pa tientia nostra? quamdiu nos etiam fu ror iste tuus eludet? quem ad finem se se effrenata jactabit audacia? nihilne te nocturnum præsidium palatii, nihil urbis vigiliæ, nihil timor populi, nihil consensus bonorum omnium, nihil hic munitissimus habendi senatus locus, ni hil horum ora vultusque moverunt? pa tere tua consilia non sentis? constrict am jam omnium horum conscientia ten eri conjurationem tuam non vides?

ABCDEFGHIJKLMNOPR

V. FIGGINS.

Great Primer, No.4.

Quousque tandem abutere, Catilina, patientia nostra? quamdiu nos etiam furor iste tuus eludet? quem ad finem sese effrenata jactabit audacia? nihil ne te nocturnum præsidium palatii, nihil urbis vigiliæ, nihil timor populi, nihil consensus bonorum omnium, nihil hic munitissimus habendi senatus locus, nihil horum ora vultusque moverunt? patere tua consilia non sentis? constrictam jam omnium horum conscientia teneri conjurationem

ABCDEFGHIJKLMNOPQRSTU
1234567890

Quousque tandem abutere, Catilina, patientia nostra? quamdiu nos etiam furor iste tuus eludet? quem ad finem sese effrenata jactabit audacia? nihilne te nocturnum præsidium palatii, nihil urbis vigiliæ, nihil timor populi, nihil consensus bonorum omnium, nihil hic munitissimus habendi senatus locus, nihil horum ora vultusque moverunt? patere tua consilia non sentis? constrictam jam omnium horum conscientia teneri conjurationem tuam non vides? quid proxim

ABCDEFGHIJKLMNOPQR

V. FIGGINS.

Quousque tandem abutere, Catilina,
patientia nostra? quamdiu nos etiam
furor iste tuus eludet? quem ad finem sese effrenata jactabit audacia?
nihilne te nocturnum præsidium palatii, nihil urbis vigiliæ, nihil timor
populi, nihil consensus bonorum omnium, nihil hic munitissimus habendi
senatus locus, nihil horum ora vultusque moverunt? patere tua consilia non sentis? constrictam jam omnium horum conscientia teneri conju
ABCDEFGHIJKLMNOPQR.
1234567890

Quousque tandem abutere, Catilina, pa
tientia nostra? quamdiu nos etiam fu-
ror iste tuus eludet? quem ad finem se-
se effrenata jactabit audacia? nihilne te
nocturnum præsidium palatii, nihil ur-
bis vigiliæ, nihil timor populi, nihil con
sensus bonorum omnium, nihil hic muni
tissimus habendi senatus locus, nihil ho
rum ora vultusque moverunt? patere tua
consilia non sentis? constrictam jam
omnium horum conscientia teneri conju-
rationem tuam non vides? quid proxim
ABCDEFGHIJKLMNOPQR

V. FIGGINS.

Quousque tandem abutere, Catilina, patientia nostra? quamdiu nos etiam furor is te tuus eludet? quem ad finem sese effrenata jactabit audacia? nihilne te nocturnum præsidium palatii, nihil urbis vigiliæ, nihil timor populi, nihil consensus bonorum omnium, nihil hic munitissimus habendi senatus locus, nihil horum ora vultusque moverunt? patere tua consilia non sentis? constrictam jam omnium horum conscientia teneri conjurationem tuam non vides? quid proxima, quid superiore nocte egeris, ubi fueris, quos convocaveris? quid consilii ceperis, quem nostrum igno-
ABCDEFGHIJKLMNOPQRSTUVWX
1234567890

Quousque tandem abutere, Catilina, patien tia nostra? quamdiu nos etiam furor iste tu us eludet? quem ad finem sese effrenata jac tabit audacia? nihilne te nocturnum præsi dium patatii, nihil urbis vigiliæ, nihil timor populi, nihil consensus bonorum omnium, ni hil hic munitissimus habendi senatus locus, nihil horum ora vultusque moverunt? patere tua consilii non sentis? constrictam jam om nium horum conscientia teneri conjuratio nem tuam non vides? quid proxima quid su periore nocte egeris, ubi fueris, quos convo caveris? quid consilii ceperis, quem nostrum ignorare arbitraris? O tempora o mores?
ABCDEFGHIJKLMNOPQRSTUV

V. FIGGINS.

Quousque tandem abutere, Catilina, patientia nostra? quamdiu nos etiam furor iste tu
us eludet? quem ad finem sese effrenata jac
tabit audacia? nihilne te nocturnum præsidium palatii, nihil urbis vigiliæ, nihil timor
populi nihil consensus bonorum omnium, nihil hic munitissimus habendi senatus locus,
nihil horum ora vultusque moverunt? patere
tua consilia non sentis? constrictam jam om
nium horum conscientia teneri conjurationem tuam non vides? quid proxima, quid su
periore nocte egeris, ubi fueris, quos convocaveris, quid consilii ceperis, quem nostrum
ignorare arbitraris? O tempora, o mores!
Senatus hoc intelligit, consul vidit: hic tamen vivit. Vivit? imo vero etiam in sena-
ABCDEFGHIJKLNOPQRSTUVW

Quousque tandem abutere, Catilina, patien
tia nostra? quamdiu nos etiam furor iste tuus
eludet? quem ad finem sese effrenata jactabit
audacia? nihilne te nocturnum præsidium pa
latii, nihil urbis vigiliæ, nihil timor populi
nihil consensus bonorum omnium, nihil hic
munitissimus habendi senatus locus, nihil ho
rum ora vultusque moverunt? patere tua con
silia non sentis? constrictam jam omnium ho
rum conscientia teneri conjurationem tuam
non vides? quid proxima, quid superiore noc
te egeris, ubi fueris, quos convocaveris, quid
consilii ceperis, quem nostrum ignorare arbi
traris? O tempora, o mores! Senatus hoc in
telligit, consul vidit: hic tamen vivit. vivit?
imo vero etiam in senatum venit fit publici
ABCDEFGHIJKLMNOPQRSTU

V. Figgins.

English, No. 5.

Quousque tandem abutere, Catilina, patien
tia nostra? quamdiu nos etiam furor iste tu
us eludet? quem ad finem sese effrenata
jactabit audacia? nihilne te nocturnum præ
sidium palatii, nihil urbis vigiliæ, nihil timor populi, nihil consensus bonorum om
nium, nihil hic munitissimus habendi sena
tus locus nihil horum ora vultusque move
runt? patere tua consilia non sentis? con
strictam jam omnium horum conscientia te
neri conjurationem tuam non vides? quid
proxima, quid superiore, nocte egeris, ubi
fueris, quos convocaveris, quid consilii ce
peris, quem nostrum ignorare arbitraris? O
tempora, o mores! Senatus hoc intelligit,
consul vidit: hic tamen vivit. Vivit? imo
ABCDEFGHIJKLMNOPQRSTUV

Quousque tandem abutere, Catilina, patien-
tia nostra? quamdiu nos etiam furor iste tu-
us eludet? quem ad finem sese effrenata jacta
bit audacia? nihilne te nocturnum præsidium
palatii, nihil urbis vigiliæ, nihil timor populi
nihil consensus bonorum omnium, nihil hic mu
nitissimus habendi senatus locus, nihil horum
ora vultusque moverunt? patere tua consilia
non sentis? constrictam jam omnium horum
conscientia teneri conjurationem tuam non vi-
des? quid proxima, quid superiore, nocte ege
ris, ubi fueris, quos convocaveris, quid consi-
lii ceperis quem nostrum ignorare arbitraris?
O tempora o mores! Senatus hoc intelligit
consul vidit: hic tamen vivit. Vivit? imo ve
ro etiam in senatum venit: fit publici consilii
ABCDEFGHIJKLMNOPQRSTUW.

V. FIGGINS.

Quousque tandem abutere, Catilina, patientia nostra? quamdiu nos etiam furor iste tu
us eludet? quem ad finem sese effrenata jac
tabit audacia? nihilne te nocturnum præsidium palatii, nihil urbis vigiliæ, nihil timor
populi, nihil consensus bonorum omnium,
nihil hic munitissimus habendi senatus locus
nihil horum ora vultusque moverunt? patere
tua consilia non sentis? constrictam jam om
nium horum conscientia teneri conjurationem
tuam non vides? quid proxima, quid superi
ore nocte egeris, ubi fueris, quos convocave
ris, quid consilii ceperis, quem nostrum ignorare arbitraris? O tempora, o mores! Senatus hoc intelligit, consul vidit: hic tamen
vivit. Vivit? imo vero etiam in senatum ve-
ABCDEFGHIJKLMNOPQRSTUV
1234567890

Quousque tandem abutere, Catilina, patien
tia nostra? quamdiu nos etiam furor iste tuus
eludet? quem ad finem sese effrenata jactabit
audacia? nihilne te nocturnum præsidium pa
latii, nihil urbis vigiliæ, nihil timor populi
nihil consensus bonorum omnium, nihil hic
munitissimus habendi senatus locus, nihil ho
rum ora vultusque moverunt? patere tua con
silia non sentis? constrictam jam omnium ho
rum conscientia teneri conjurationem tuam
non vides? quid proxima, quid superiore noc
te egeris, ubi fueris, quos convocaveris, quid
consilii ceperis, quem nostrum ignorare arbi
traris? O tempora, o mores! Senatus hoc in
telligit, consul vidit: hic tamen vivit. vivit?
imo vero etiam in senatum venit fit publici
ABCDEFGHIJKLMNOPQRSTU

V. Figgins.

Quousque tandem abutere, Catilina, patientia nostra? quamdiu nos etiam furor iste tuus eludet? quem ad finem sese effrenata jactabit audacia? nihilne te nocturnum præsidium palatii, nihil urbis vigiliæ, nihil timor populi, nihil consensus bonorum omnium, nihil hic munitissimus habendi senatus locus, nihil horum ora vultusque moverunt? patere tua consilia non sentis? constrictam jam omnium horum conscientia teneri conjurationem tuam non vides? quid proxima, quid superiore, nocte egeris, ubi fueris, quos convocaveris, quid consilii ceperis, quem nostrum ignorare arbitraris? O tempora, o mores! Senatus hoc intelligit, consul vidit: hic tamen vivit. Vivit? imo vero etiam in senatum venit: fit publici consilii particeps: notat et designat oculis ad cædem unumquemque nostrum. Nos autem viri fortes sa tisfacere reipublicæ videmur, si istius furorem ac tela vitemus. Ad mortem te, Catilina duci jussu con

ABCDEFGHIJKLMNOPQRSTUVWXY

Quousque tandem abutere, Catilina, patientia nostra? quamdiu nos etiam furor iste tuus eludet? quem ad finem sese effrenata jactabit audacia? nihilne te nocturnum præsidium palatii, nihil urbis vigiliæ, nihil timor populi, nihil consensus bonorum omnium, nihil hic munitissimus habendi senatus locus, nihil horum ora vultusque moverunt? patere tua consilia non sentis? constrictam jam omnium horum conscientia teneri conjurationem tuam non vides? quid proxima, quid superiore, nocte egeris, ubi fueris, quos convocaveris, quid consilii ceperis, quem nostrum ignorare arbitraris? O tempora, o mores! Se natus hoc intelligit, consul vidit: hic tamen vivit. Vivit? imo vero etiam in senatum venit: fit publici consilii particeps: notat et designat oculis ad cædem unumquemque nostrum. Nos autem viri fortes satisfacere reipublicæ videmur, si istius furorem ac tela vitemus. Ad mortem te, Catilina, duci jussu

ABCDEFGHIJKLMNOPQRSTUVW

V. FIGGINS.

Pica, No. 4.

Quousque tandem abutere, Catilina, patientia nostra? quamdiu nos etiam furor iste tuus eludet? quem ad finem sese effrenata jactabit audacia? nihilne te nocturnum præsidium palatii, nihil urbis vigiliæ, nihil timor populi, nihil consensus bonorum omnium, nihil hic munitissimus habendi senatus locus nihil horum ora vultusque moverunt? patere tua consilia non sentis? constrictam jam omnium horum conscientia teneri conjurationem tuam non vides? quid proxima, quid superiore, nocte egeris, ubi fueris, quos convocaveris, quid consilii ceperis, quem nostrum ignorare arbitraris? O tempora, o mores! Senatus hoc intelligit, consul vidit: hic tamen vivit. Vivit? imo vero etiam in senatum venit: fit publici consilii particeps: notat et designat oculis ad cædem unumquemque nostrum. Nos autem viri fortes satisfacere reipublicæ videmur si istius furorem ac tela vitemus. Ad mortem te Catilina duci jussu

ABCDEFGHIJKLMNOPQRSTUVWXY
1234567890

Quousque tandem abutere, Catilina, patientia nostra? quamdiu nos etiam furor iste tuus eludet? quem ad finem sese effrenata jactabit audacia? ni hilne te nocturnum præsidium palatii, nihil urbis vigiliæ, nihil timor populi, nihil consensus bonorum omnium, nihil hic munitissimus habendi senatus locus, nihil horum ora vultusque moverunt? patere tua consilia non sentis? constrictam jam omnium horum conscientia teneri conjurationem tuam non vides? quid proxima, quid superiore nocte egeris, ubi fueris, quos convocaveris, quid consilii ceperis, quem nostrum ignorare arbitraris? O tempora, o mores! Senatus hoc intelligit, consul vidit: hic ta men vivit. Vivit? imo vero etiam in senatum venit: fit publici consilii particeps: notat et designat oculis ad cædem unumquemque nostrum. Nos autem viri fortes satisfacere reipublicæ videmur, si istius furorem ac tela vitemus. Ad mortem te, Cati

ABCDEFGHIJKLMNOPQRSTUWX

V. FIGGINS.

Pica, No. 6.

Quousque tandem abutere, Catilina, patientia nos
tra? quamdiu nos etiam furor iste tuus eludet?
quem ad finem sese effrenata jactabit audacia? ni
hilne te nocturnum præsidium palatii, nihil urbis
vigiliæ, nihil timor populi, nihil consensus bonorum omnium, nihil hic munitissimus habendi sena
tus locus, nihil horum ora vultusque moverunt?
patere tua consilia non sentis? constrictam jam
omnium horum conscientia teneri conjurationem
tuam non vides? quid proxima, quid superiore noc
te egeris, ubi fueris, quos convocaveris, quid con
silii ceperis, quem nostrum ignorare arbitraris? O
tempore, o mores! Senatus hoc intelligit, consul
vidit : hic tamen vivit. Vivit? imo vero etiam in
senatum venit : fit publici consilii particeps : notat et designat oculis ad cædem unumquemque
nostrum. Nos autem viri fortes satisfacere reipub
licæ videmur, si istius furorem ac tela vitemus. Ad

ABCDEFGHIJKLMNOPQRSTUVWXY
1234567890

Quousque tandem abutere, Catilina, patientia nos-
tra? quamdiu nos etiam furor iste tuus eludet? quem
ad finem sese effrenata jactabit audacia? nihilne te
nocturnum præsidium palatii, nihil urbis vigiliæ, ni-
hil timor populi, nihil consensus bonorum omnium,
nihil hic munitissimus habendi senatus locus, nihil
horum ora vultusque moverunt? patere tua consilia
non sentis? constrictam jam omnium horum consci-
entia teneri conjurationem tuam non vides? quid
proxima, quid superiore, nocte egeris, ubi fueris,
quos convocaveris, quid consilii ceperis, quem nos-
trum ignorare arbitraris? O tempora, o mores! Se-
natus hoc intelligit, consul vidit : hic tamen vivit.
Vivit? imo vero etiam in senatum venit: fit publici
consilii particeps : notat et designat oculis ad cæ-
dem unumquemque nostrum. Nos autem viri fortes
satisfacere reipublicæ videmur, si istius furorem ac
tela vitemus. Ad mortem te, Catilina, duci jussu

ABCDEFGHIJKLMNOPQRSTUVW

V. FIGGINS.

Pica, No. 7.

Quousque tandem abutere, Catilina patientia nos
tra? quamdiu nos etiam furor iste tuus eludet?
quem ad finem sese effrenata jactabit audacia? ni
hilne te nocturnum præsidium palatii, nihil urbis
vigiliæ, nihil timor populi, nihil consensus bonorum omnium nihil hic munitissimus habendi senatus locus, horum ora vultusque moverunt? patere tua consilia non sentis? constrictam jam om
nium horum conscientia teneri conjurationem tu
am non vides? quid proxima, quid superiore nocte egeris, ubi fueris quos convocaveris, quid consilii ceperis, quem nostrum ignorare arbitraris?
O tempora, o mores! Senatus hoc intelligit, consul videt: hic tamen vivit. Vivit? imo vero etiam
in senatum venit: fit publici consilii particeps:
notat et designat oculis ad cædem unumquemque nostrum. Nos autem, viri fortes, satisfacere
republicæ videmur si istius furorem ac tela vite-
ABCDEFGHIJKLMNOPQRSTUVWX
1234567890

Quousque tandem abutere, Catilina, patientia nos-
tra? quamdiu nos etiam furor iste tuus eludet? quem
ad finem sese effrenata jactabit audacia? nihilne te
nocturnum præsidium palatii, nihil urbis vigiliæ, ni-
hil timor populi, nihil consensus bonorum omnium,
nihil hic munitissimus habendi senatus locus, nihil
horum ora vultusque moverunt? patere tua consilia
non sentis? constrictam jam omnium horum consci-
entia teneri conjurationem tuam non vides? quid
proxima, quid superiore, nocte egeris, ubi fueris,
quos convocaveris, quid consilii ceperis, quem nos-
trum ignorare arbitraris? O tempora, o mores! Se
natus hoc intelligit, consul vidit: hic tamen vivit.
Vivit? imo vero etiam in senatum venit: fit publici
consilii particeps: notat et designat oculis ad cæ-
dem unumquemque nostrum. Nos autem viri fortes
satisfacere reipublicæ videmur, si istius furorem ac
tela vitemus. Ad mortem te, Catilina, duci jussu
ABCDEFGHIJKLMNOPQRSTUVW

V. FIGGINS.

Small Pica, No. 2.

Quousque tandem abutere, Catilina, patientia nostra? quamdiu nos etiam furor iste tuus eludet? quem ad finem sese effrenata jactabit audacia? nihilne te nocturnum præsidium palatii, nihil urbis vigiliæ, nihil timor populi, nihil consensus bonorum omnium, nihil hic munitissimus habendi senatus locus, nihil horum ora vultusque moverunt? patere tua consilia non sentis? constrictam jam omnium horum conscientia teneri conjurationem tuam non vides? quid proxima, quid superiore nocte egeris, ubi fueris, quos convocaveris, quid consilii ceperis, quem nostrum ignorare arbitraris? O tempora, o mores! Senatus hoc intelligit, consul vidit: hic tamen vivit. Vivit? imo vero etiam in senatum venit: fit publici consilii particeps: notat et designat oculis ad cædem unumquemque nostrum. Nos autem viri fortes satisfacere reipublicæ videmur, si istius furorem ac tela vitemus. Ad mortem te, Catilina, duci jussu consulis jam pridem oportebat: in te conferri pestem istam, quam tu in nos omnes jamdiu machinaris. An vero vir amplissimus, P. Scipio, pontifex maximus, Tiberium Gracchum mediocriter labefactantem statum reipublicæ privatus interfecit: Catilinam vero orbem terræ cæde atque incendiis vastare cupientem nos
ABCDEFGHIJKLMNOPQRSTUVWXYZÆŒ.
1234567890.

Quousque tandem abutere, Catilina, patientia nostra? quamdiu nos etiam furor iste tuus eludet? quem ad finem sese effrenata jactabit audacia? nihilne te nocturnum præsidium palatii, nihil urbis vigiliæ, nihil timor populi, nihil consensus bonorum omnium, nihil hic munitissimus habendi senatus locus, nihil horum ora vultusque moverunt? patere tua consilia non sentis? constrictam jam omnium horum conscientia teneri conjurationem tuam non vides? quid proxima, quid superiore, nocte egeris, ubi fueris, quos convocaveris, quid consilii ceperis, quem nostrum ignorare arbitraris? O tempora, o mores! Senatus hoc intelligit, consul vidit: hic tamen vivit. Vivit? imo vero etiam in senatum venit: fit publici consilii particeps: notat et designat oculis ad cædem unumquemque nostrum. Nos autem viri fortes satisfacere reipublicæ videmur, si istius furorem ac tela vitemus. Ad mortem te, Catilina, duci jussu consulis jam pridem oportebat: in te conferri pestem istam, quam tu in nos omnes jamdiu machinaris. An vero vir amplissimus, P. Scipio, pontifex maximus Tiberium Gracchum mediocriter labefactantum statum reipublicæ priva-
ABCDEFGHIJKLMNOPQRSTUVWXYZ
V. Figgins.

Small Pica, No. 4.

Quousque tandem abutere, Catilina, patientia nostra? quamdiu nos etiam furor iste tuus eludet? quem ad finem sese effrenata jactabit audacia? nihilne te nocturnum præsidium palatii, nihil urbis vigiliæ, nihil timor populi, nihil consensus bonorum omnium nihil hic munitissimus habendi senatus locus, nihil horum ora vultusque moverunt? patere tua consilia non sentis? constrictam jam omnium horum conscientia teneri conjurationem tuam non vides? quid proxima, quid superi ore nocte egeris, ubi fueris, quos convocaveris quid con sili ceperis, quem nostrum ignorare arbitraris? O tempora, o mores! Senatus hoc intelligit, consul vidit: hic tamen vivit. Vivit? imo vero etiam in senatum venit: fit publici consilii particeps: notat et designat oculis ad cædem unumquemque nostrum. Nos autem, viri, for tes, satisfacere reipub. videmur si istius furorem ac tela vitemus. Ad mortem te, Catilina, duci jussu consulis jampridem oportebat: in te conferri pestem istam, quam tu in nos omnes jamdiu machinaris. An vero vir amplissimus, P. Scipio. pontifex maximus. Tiberium Grac chum, mediocriter labefactantem statum reipublicæ, pri

ABCDEFGHIJKLMNOPQRSTUVWXYZŒ

1234567890

Quousque tandem abutere, Catilina, patientia nostra? quamdiu nos etiam furor iste tuus eludet? quem ad finem sese effrenata jactabit audacia? nihilne te nocturnum præsidium palatii, nihil urbis vigiliæ, nihil timor populi, nihil consensus bonorum omnium, nihil hic munitissimus habendi senatus locus, nihil horum ora vultusque moverunt? patere tua consilia non sentis? constrictam jam omnium horum conscientia teneri conjurationem tuam non vides? quid proxima, quid superiore, nocte egeris, ubi fueris, quos convocaveris, quid consilii ceperis, quem nostrum ignorare arbitraris? O tempora, o mores! Senatus hoc intelligit, consul vidit: hic tamen vivit. Vivit? imo vero etiam in senatum venit: fit publici consilii particeps: notat et desig nat oculis ad cædem unumquemque nostrum. Nos autem viri fortes satisfacere reipublicæ videmur, si istius furorem ac tela vitemus. Ad mortem te, Catilina, duci jussu consulis jam pridem oportebat: in te conferri pestem istam, quam tu in nos omnes jamdiu machinaris. An vero vir amplissimus, P. Scipio, pontifex maximus Tiberium Gracchum mediocriter labefactantum statum reipublicæ priva-

ABCDEFGHIJKLMNOPQRSTUVWXYZ

V. FIGGINS.

Quousque tandem abutere, Catilina, patientia nostra? quamdiu nos etiam furor iste tuus eludet? quem ad finem sese effrenata jactabit audacia? nihilne te nocturnum præsidium palatii, nihil urbis vigiliæ, nihil timor populi, nihil consensus bonorum omnium, nihil hic munitissimus habendi senatus locus, nihil horum ora vultusque moverunt? patere tua consilia non sentis? constrictam jam omnium horum conscientia teneri conjurationem tuam non vides? quid proxima, quid superiore nocte egeris, ubi fueris, quos convocaveris, quid consilii ceperis, quem nostrum ignorare arbitraris? O tempora, o mores! Senatus hoc intelligit, consul vidit: hic tamen vivit. Vivit imo vero etiam in senatum venit: fit publici consilii par ticeps: notat et designat oculis ad cædem unumquemque nostrum. Nos autem viri fortes satisfacere reipublicæ videmur, si istius furorem ac tela vitemus. Ad mortem te Catilina duci jussu consulis jampridem oportebat: in te conferri pestem istam, quam tu in nos omnes jamdiu machinaris. An vero vir amplissimus P. Scipio, pontifex maximus, Tiberium Gracchum mediocriter labefactantem statum reipublicæ privatus interfecit: Catilinam ve

ABCDEFGHIJKLMNOPQRSTUVWXYZÆŒ
1234567890.

Quousque tandem abutere, Catilina, patientia nostra? quamdiu nos etiam furor iste tuus eludet? quem ad finem sese effrenata jactabit audacia? nihilne te nocturnum præsidium palatii, nihil urbis vigiliæ, nihil timor populi, nihil consensus bonorum omnium, nihil hic munitissimus habendi senatus locus, nihil horum ora vultusque moverunt? patere tua consilia non sentis? constrictam jam omnium horum conscientia teneri conjurationem tuam non vides? quid proxima, quid superiore, nocte egeris, ubi fueris, quos convocaveris, quid consilii ceperis, quem nostrum ignorare arbitraris? O tempora, o mores! Senatus hoc intelligit, consul vidit: hic tamen vivit. Vivit? imo vero etiam in senatum venit: fit publici consilii particeps: notat et designat oculis ad cædem unumquemque nostrum. Nos autem viri fortes satisfacere reipublicæ videmur, si istius furorem ac tela vitemus. Ad mortem te, Catilina, duci jussu consulis jam pridem oportebat: in te conferri pestem istam, quam tu in nos omnes jamdiu machinaris. An vero vir amplissimus, P. Scipio, pontifex maximus Tiberium Gracchum mediocriter labefactantum statum reipublicæ priva-

ABCDEFGHIJKLMNOPQRSTUVWXYZ

V. FIGGINS.

Long Primer, No. 2.

Quousque tandem abutere, Catilina, patientia nostra? quamdiu nos etiam furor iste tuus eludet? quem ad finem sese effrenata jactabit audacia? nihilne te nocturnum præsidium palatii, nihil urbis vigiliæ, nihil timor populi, nihil consensus bonorum omnium, nihil hic munitissimus habendi senatus locus, nihil horum ora vultusque moverunt? patere tua consilia non sentis? constrictam jam omnium horum conscientia teneri conjurationem tuam non vides? quid proxima, quid superiore, nocte egeris, ubi fueris, quos convocaveris, quid consilii ceperis, quem nostrum ignorare arbitraris? O tempora, o mores! Senatus hoc intelligit, consul vidit: hic tamen vivit. Vivit? imo vero etiam in senatum venit: fit publici consilii particeps: notat et designat oculis ad cædem unumquemque nostrum. Nos autem viri fortes satisfacere reipublicæ videmur, si istius furorem ac tela vi-

ABCDEFGHIJKLMNOPQRSTUVWXYZÆŒ.
1234567890.

No. 3.

Quousque tandem abutere, Catilina, patientia nostra? quamdiu nos etiam furor iste tuus eludet? quem ad finem sese effrenata jactabit audacia? nihilne te nocturnum præsidium palatii, nihil urbis vigiliæ, nihil timor populi, nihil consensus bonorum omnium, nihil hic munitissimus habendi senatus locus, nihil horum ora vultusque moverunt? patere tua consilia non sentis? constrictam jam omnium horum conscientia teneri conjurationem tuam non vides? quid proxima, quid superiore, nocte egeris, ubi fueris, quos convocaveris, quid consilii ceperis, quem nostrum ignorare arbitraris? O tempora, o mores! Senatus hoc intelligit, consul vidit: hic tamen vivit. Vivit? imo vero etiam in senatum venit: fit publici consilii particeps: notat et designat oculis ad cædem unumquemque nostrum. Nos autem viri fortes satisfacere reipublicæ videmur, si istius furorem ac tela vitemus. Ad mortem te

ABCDEFGHIJKLMNOPQRSTUVWXYZÆŒ
1234567890.

Quousque tandem abutere, Catilina patientia nostra? quamdiu nos etiam furor iste tuus eludet? quem ad finem sese effrenata jactabit audacia? nihilne te nocturnum præsidium palatii, nihil urbis vigiliæ, nihil timor populi, nihil consensus bonorum omnium, nihil hic munitissimus habendi senatus locus, nihil horum ora vultusque moverunt? patere tua consilia non sentis? constrictam jam omnium horum conscientia teneri conjurationem tuam non vides? quid proxima, quid superiore, nocte egeris, ubi fueris, quos convocaveris, quid consilii ceperis, quem nostrum ignorare arbitraris? O tempora, o mores! Senatus hoc intelligit, consul vidit: hic tamen vivit. Vivit? imo vero etiam in senatum venit: fit publici consilii particeps: notat et designat oculis ad cædem unumquemque nostrum. Nos autem viri fortes satisfacere reipublicæ videmur, si istius furorem ac

ABCDEFGHIJKLMNOPQRSTUVWXYZÆŒ.

V. Figgins.

Long Primer, No. 6.

Quousque tandem abutere, Catilina, patientia nostra? quamdiu nos etiam furor iste tuus eludet? quem ad finem sese effrenata jac tabit audacia? nihilne te nocturnum præsidium palatii, nihil urbis vigiliæ, nihil timor populi, nihil consensus bonorum omnium, nihil hic munitissimus habendi senatus locus, nihil horum ora vul tusque moverunt? patere tua consilia non sentis? constrictam jam omnium horum conscientia tenèri conjurationem tuam non vides? quid proxima, quid superiore, nocte egeris, ubi fueris, quos convocaveris, quid consilii ceperis, quem nostrum ignorare arbitraris? O tempora, o mores! Senatus hoc intelligit, consul vidit: hic tamen vivit. Vivit? imo vero etiam in senatum venit? fit publici consilii particeps: notat et designat oculis ad cædem unumquemque nostrum. Nos autem viri fortes satisfacere reipublicæ videmur, si istius furorem ac tela vitemus. Ad mortem te, Catilina, duci jussu consulis jampridem oportebat: in te conferri pestem istam, quam tu in nos omnes jamdiu machinaris. An vero vir amplissimus, P. Scipio, pontifex maximus, Tiberium Gracchum mediocriter labefactantem statum reipublicæ privatus interfecit: Catilinam vero orbem terræ cæde atque incendiis vastare cupientem nos consules perferemus? nam illa nimis antiqua prætereo, quod Quintus Servilius Ahala Sp. Melium, novis rebus stu dentum manu suo occidit.

ABCDEFGHIJKLMNOPQRSTUVWXYZÆŒ

1234567890

Quousque tandem abutere, Catilina, patientia nostra? quamdiu nos etiam furor iste tuus eludet? quem ad finem sese effrenata jactabit audacia? nihilne te nocturnum præsidium palatii, nihil urbis vigiliæ, nihil timor populi, nihil consensus bonorum omnium, nihil hic munitissimus habendi senatus locus, nihil horum ora vultusque moverunt? patere tua consilia non sentis? constrictam jam omnium horum conscientia teneri conjurationem tuam non vides? quid prox ima, quid superiore, nocte egeris, ubi fueris, quos convocaveris, quid consilii ceperis, quem nostrum ignorare arbitraris? O tempora, o mores! Senatus hoc intelligit, consul vidit: hic tamen vivit. Vivit? imo vero etiam in senatum venit: fit publici consilii particeps: notat et designat oculis ad cædem unumquemque nostrum. Nos autem viri fortes satisfacere reipublicæ videmur, si istius furo rem ac tela vitemus. Ad mortem te, Catilina, duci jussu consulis jampridem oportebat: in te conferri pestem istam, quam tu in nos omnes jamdiu machinaris. An vero vir amplissimus, P. Scipio, pontifex maximus, Tiberium Gracchum mediocriter labefactantem statum reipublicæ privatus interfecit: Catilinam vero orbem terræ cæde atque incendiis vastare cupientem nos consules perferemus? nam illa nimis antiqua prætereo, quod Quintus Servilius Ahala Sp. Melium, novis rebus studentem manu suo occidit.

ABCDEFGHIJKLMNOPQRSTUVWXYZÆŒ

V. FIGGINS.

Bourgeois, No. 3.

Quousque tandem abutere, Catilina, patientia nostra? quamdiu nos etiam furor iste tuus eludet? quem ad finem sese effrenata jactabit audacia? nihilne te nocturnum præsidium palatii, nihil urbis vigiliæ, nihil timor populi, nihil consensus bonorum omnium, nihil hic munitissimus habendi senatus locus, nihil horum ora vultusque moverunt? patere tua consilia non sentis? constrictam jam omnium horum conscientia teneri conjurationem tuam non vides? quid proxima, quid superiore nocte egeris, ubi fueris, quos convocaveris, quid consilii ceperis, quem nostrum ignorare arbitraris? O tempora, o mores! Senatus hoc intelligit, consul vidit: hic tamen vivit. Vivit? imo vero etiam in senatum venit: fit publici consilii particeps: notat et designat ocu lis ad cædem unumquemque nostrum. Nos autem, viri fortes, satisfacere reipublicæ videmur, si istius furorem ac tela vitemus. Ad mor tem te, Catilina, duci jussu consulis jampridem oportebat: in te conferri pestem istam, quam tu in nos omnes jamdiu machinaris. An vero vir amplissimus, P. Scipio, pontifex maximus, Tiberium Gracchum mediocriter labefactantem statum reipublicæ privatus interfecit: Catilinam vero orbem terræ cæde atque incendiis vastare cupientem nos consules perferemus? nam illa nimis antiqua prætereo, quod Quintus Servilius Ahala Sp. Melium, novis rebus studentum manu suo occidit.

ABCDEFGHIJKLMNOPQRSTUVWXYZÆŒ

1234567890

Quousque tandem abutere, Catilina, patientia nostra? quamdiu nos etiam furor iste tuus eludet? quem ad finem sese effrenata jactabit audacia? nihilne te nocturnum præsidium palatii, nihil urbis vigiliæ, nihil timor populi, nihil consensus bonorum omnium, nihil hic munitissimus habendi senatus locus, nihil horum ora vultusque moverunt? patere tua consilia non sentis? constrictam jam omnium horum conscientia teneri conjurationem tuam non vides? quid proxima, quid superiore, nocte egeris, ubi fueris, quos convocaveris, quid consilii ceperis, quem nostrum ignorare arbitraris? O tempora, o mores! Senatus hoc intelligit, consul vidit: hic tamen vivit. Vivit? imo vero etiam in senatum venit? fit publici consilii particeps: notat et designat oculis ad cædem unumquemque nostrum. Nos autem viri fortes satisfacere reipublicæ videmur, si istius furorem ac tela vitemus. Ad mortem te, Catilina, duci jussu consulis jampridem oportebat: in te conferri pestem istam, quam tu in nos omnes jamdiu machinaris. An vero vir amplissimus, P. Scipio, pontifex maximus, Tiberium Gracchum mediocriter labefactantem statum reipublicæ privatus interfecit: Catilinam vero orbem terræ cæde atque incendiis vastare cupientem nos consules perferemus? nam illa nimis antiqua prætereo, quod Quintus Servilius Ahala Sp. Melium, novis rebus studentum manu suo occidit. Fuit, fuit ista quondam, in hac republica vir

ABCDEFGHIJKLMNOPQRSTUVWXYZÆŒ

V. Figgins.

Quousque tandem abutere, Catilina, patientia nostra? quamdiu nos etiam furor iste tuus eludet? quem ad finem sese effrenata jactabit audacia? nihilne te nocturnum præsidium palatii, nihil urbis vigiliæ, nihil timor popu li, nihil consensus bonorum omnium, nihil hic munitissimus habendi senatus locus, nihil horum ora vultusque moverunt? patere tua consilia non sen tis? constrictam jam omnium horum conscientia teneri conjurationem tuam non vides? quid proxima, quid superiore nocte egeris, ubi fueris, quos convocaveris, quid consilii ceperis, quem nostrum ignorare arbitraris? O tem pora, o mores! Senatus hoc intelligit, consul vidit: hic tamen vivit. Vivit imo vero etiam in senatum venit: fit publici consilii particeps notat et desig nat oculis ad cædem unumquemque nostrum. Nos autem viri fortes satisfacere reipublicæ videmur, si istius furorem ac tela vitemus. Ad mortem te,

ABCDEFGHIJKLMNOPQRSTUVWXYZÆŒ.
1234567890   1234567890

Quousque tandem abutere, Catilina, patientia nostra? quamdiu nos etiam furor iste tuus eludet? quem ad finem sese effrenata jactabit audacia? nihilne te nocturnum præsidium palatii, nihil urbis vigiliæ, nihil timor populi, nihil consensus bonorum omnium, nihil hic munitissimus habendi senatus locus, nihil horum ora vultusque moverunt? patere tua consilia non sentis? constrictam jam omnium horum conscientia teneri conjurationem tuam non vides? quid proxima quid superiore nocte egeris, ubi fueris, quos convocaveris, quid consilii ceperis, quem nostrum ignorare arbitraris? O tempora, o mores! Senatus hoc intelligit consul vidit: hic tamen vivit. Vivit? imo vero etiam in senatum venit: fit publici consilii particeps notat et designat oculis ad cædem unumquemque nostrum. Nos autem viri fortes satisfacere reipublicæ videmur, si istius furorem ac tela vitemus, Ad mortem te, Catilina duci jussu consulis jampridem opor-

ABCDEFGHIJKLMNOPQRSTUWXYZÆŒ.

Quousque tandem abutere, Catilina, patientia nostra? quamdiu nos etiam furor iste tuus eludet? quem ad finem sese effrenata jactabit audacia? ni hilne te nocturnum præsidium palatii, nihil urbis vigiliæ, nihil timor populi, nihil consensus bonorum omnium, nihil hic munitissimus habendi se natus locus, nihil horum ora vultusque moverunt? patere tua consilia non sentis? constrictam jam omnium horum conscientia teneri conjurationem tuam non vides? quid proxima, quid superiore nocte egeris, ubi fueris, quos convocaveris, quid consilii ceperis, quem nostrum ignorare arbitraris O tempora, o mores! Senatus hoc intelligit, consul vidit: hic tamen vivit Vivit? imo vero etiam in senatum venit: fit publici consilii particeps notat et designat oculis ad cædem unumquemque nostrum. Nos autem viri fortes satisfacere reipublicæ videmur, si istius furorem ac tela vitemus. Ad

ABCDEFGHIJKLMNOPQRSTUVWXYZÆŒ
1234567890   1234567890

Quousque tandem abutere, Catilina, patientia nostra? quamdiu nos etiam furor iste tuus eludet? quem ad finem sese effrenata jactabit audacia? ni hilne te nocturnum præsidium palatii, nihil urbis vigiliæ, nihil timor populi, nihil consensus bonorum omnium, nihil hic munitissimus habendi senatus locus, nihil horum ora vultusque moverunt? patere tua consilia non sentis? constrictam jam omnium horum conscientia teneri conjurationem tuam non vides? quid proxima, quid superiore nocte egeris, ubi fueris, quos convocaveris, quid consilii ceperis, quem nostrum ignorare arbitraris? O tempora o mores! Senatus hoc intelligit, consul vidit: hic tamen vivit. Vivit? imo vero etiam in senatum venit: fit publici consilii particeps: notat et designat oculis ad cædem unumquemque nostrum. Nos autem viri fortes satisfacere reipublicæ videmur, si istius furorem ac tela vitemus. Ad mortem te

ABCDEFGHIJKLMNOPQRSTUVWXYZÆŒ

V. FIGGINS.

Brevier, No. 4.

Quousque tandem abutere, Catilina, patientia nostra? quamdiu nos etiam furor iste tuus eludet? quem ad finem sese effrenata jactabit audacia? nihilne te nocturnum præsidium palatii, nihil urbis vigiliæ, nihil timor populi, nihil consensus bonorum omnium, nihil hic munitissimus habendi senatus locus, nihil horum ora vultusque moverunt? patere tua consilia non sentis? constrictam jam omnium horum conscientia teneri conjurationem tuam non vides quid proxima, quid superiore, nocte egeris, ubi fueris, quos convocaveris, quid consilii ceperis, quem nostrum ignorare arbitraris? O tempora, o mores! Senatus hoc intelligit, consul vidit: hic tamen vivit. Vivit? imo vero etiam in senatum venit: fit publici consilii particeps: notat et designat oculis ad cædem unumquemque nostrum. Nos autem viri fortes satisfacere reipublicæ videmur, si istius furorem ac tela vitemus. Ad mortem te, Catilina, duci jussu

ABCDEFGHIJKLMNOPQRSTUVWXYZÆŒ
1234567890

Quousque tandem abutere, Catilina, patientia nostra? quamdiu nos etiam furor iste tuus eludet? quem ad finem sese effrenata jactabit audacia? nihilne te nocturnum præsidium palatii, nihil urbis vigiliæ, nihil timor populi, nihil consensus bonorum omnium, nihil hic munitissimus habendi senatus locus, nihil horum ora vultusque moverunt? patere tua consilia non sentis? constrictam jam omnium horum conscientia teneri conjurationem tuam non vides? quid proxima, quid superiore nocte egeris, ubi fueris, quos convocaveris, quid consilii ceperis, quem nostrum ignorare arbitraris? O tempora, o mores! Senatus hoc intelligit, consul vidit: hic tamen vivit. Vivit? imo vero etiam in senatum venit: fit publici consilii particeps: notat et designat oculis ad cædem unumquemque nostrum. Nos autem viri fortes satisfacere reipublicæ videmur, si istius furorem ac tela vitemus. Ad mortem te, Catilina, duci jussu

ABCDEFGHIJKLMNOPQRSTUVWXYZÆŒ

Brevier, No. 5.

Quousque tandem abutere, Catilina, patientia nostra? quamdiu nos etiam fu ror iste tuus eludet? quem ad finem sese effrenata jactabit audacia? nihilne te nocturnum præsidium palatii, nihil urbis vigiliæ, nihil timor populi, nihil consensus bonorum omnium, nihil hic munitissimus habendi senatus locus, nihil horum ora vultusque moverunt? patere tua consilia non sentis? constrictam jam omnium horum conscientia teneri conjurationem tuam non vides? quid proxima, quid superiore nocte egeris, ubi fueris, quos convocaveris, quid consilii ceperis, quem nostrum ignorare arbitraris? O tempora, o mores! Senatus hoc intelligit, consul vidit: hic tamen vivit. Vivit? imo vero etiam in senatum venit: fit publici consilii particeps: notat et designat oculis ad cædem unumquemque nostrum. Nos autem viri fortes satisfacere reipublicæ videmur, si istius furorem ac tela vitemus. Ad mortem te, Cati-

ABCDEFGHIJKLMNOPQRSTUVWXYZÆ
1234567890

Quousque tandem abutere, Catilina, patientia nostra? quamdiu nos etiam furor iste tuus eludet? quem ad finem sese effrenata jactabit audacia? nihilne te nocturnum præsidium palatii, nihil urbis vigiliæ, nihil timor populi, nihil consensus bonorum omnium, nihil hic munitissimus habendi senatus locus, nihil horum ora vultusque moverunt? patere tua consilia non sentis? constrictam jam omnium horum conscientia teneri conjurationem tuam non vides? quid proxima, quid superiore nocte egeris, ubi fueris, quos convocaveris, quid consilii ceperis, quem nostrum ignorare arbitraris? O tempora, o mores! Senatus hoc intelligit, consul vidit: hic tamen vivit. Vivit? imo vero etiam in senatum venit: fit publici consilii particeps: notat et designat oculis ad cædem unumquemque nostrum. Nos autem viri fortes satisfacere reipublicæ videmur, si istius furorem ac tela vitemus. Ad mortem te, Catilina duci jussu

ABCDEFGHIJKLMNOPQRSTUVWXYZÆŒ

V. FIGGINS.

Minion No. 1.

Quousque tandem abutere, Catilina, patientia nostra? quamdiu nos etiam furor iste tuus eludet? quem ad finem sese effrenata jactabit audacia? nihilne te nocturnum præsidium palatii, nihil urbis vigiliæ, nihil timor populi, nihil consensus bonorum omnium, nihil hic munitissimus habendi senatus locus, nihil horum ora vultusque moverunt? patere tua consilia non sentis? constrictam jam omnium horum conscientia teneri conjurationem tuam non vides? quid proxima, quid superiore, nocte egeris, ubi fueris, quos convocaveris, quid consilii ceperis, quem nostrum ignorare, arbitraris? O tempora, o mores! Senatus hoc intelligit, consul vidit: hic tamen vivit. Vivit? imo vero etiam in senatum venit: fit publici consilii particeps: notat et designat oculis ad cædem unumquemque nostrum. Nos autem viri fortes satisfacere reipublicæ videmur, si istius furorem ac tela vitemus. Ad mortem te, Catilina, duci jussu consulis jam pridem oportebat: in te conferri pestem istam,

ABCDEFGHIJKLMNOPQRSTUXYZÆŒ
1234567890 1234567890

Quousque tandem abutere, Catilina, patientia nostra? quamdiu nos etiam furor iste tuus eludet? quem ad finem sese effrenata jactabit audacia? nihilne te nocturnum præsidium palatii, nihil urbis vigiliæ, nihil timor populi, nihil consensus bonorum omnium, nihil hic munitissimus habendi senatus locus, nihil horum ora vultusque moverunt? patere tua consilia non sentis? constrictam jam omnium horum conscientia teneri conjurationem tuam non vides? quid proxima, quid superiore, nocte egeris, ubi fueris, quos convocaveris, quid consilii ceperis, quem nostrum ignorare arbitraris? O tempora, o mores! Senatus hoc intelligit, consul vidit: hic tamen vivit? Vivit? imo vero etiam in senatum venit: fit publici consilii particeps: notat et designat oculis ad cædem unumquemque nostrum. Nos autem viri fortes satisfacere reipublicæ videmur, si istius furorem ac tela vitemus. Ad mortem te, Catilina duci, jussu consulis jam pridem oportebat: in te conferri pestem istam, quam tu in nos omnes jamdiu machinaris. An vero vir amplissi-

ABCDEFGHIJKLMNOPQRSTUVIVXYZÆŒ

Minion No. 2.

Quousque tandem abutere, Catilina, patientia nostra? quamdiu nos etiam furor iste tuus eludet? quem ad finem sese effrenata jactabit audacia? nihilne te nocturnum præsidium palatii, nihil urbis vigiliæ, nihil timor populi, nihil consensus bonorum omnium, nihil hic munitissimus habendi senatus locus, nihil horum ora vultusque moverunt? patere tua consilia non sentis? constrictam jam omnium horum conscientia teneri conjurationem tuam non vides? quid proxima, quid superiore, nocte egeris, ubi fueris, quos convocaveris, quid consilii ceperis, quem nostrum ignorare, arbitraris? O tempora, o mores! Senatus hoc intelligit, consul vidit: hic tamen vivit. Vivit? imo vero etiam in senatum venit: fit publici consilii particeps: notat et designat oculis ad cædem unumquemque nostrum. Nos autem viri fortes satisfacere reipublicæ videmur, si istius furorem ac tela vitemus. Ad mortem te, Catilina, duci jussu consulis jam pridem

ABCDEFGHIJKLMNOPQRSTUVWXYZÆŒ
1234567890 1234567890

Quousque tandem abutere, Catilina, patientia nostra? quamdiu nos etiam furor iste tuus eludet? quem ad finem sese effrenata jactabit audacia? nihilne te nocturnum præsidium palatii, nihil urbis vigiliæ, nihil timor populi, nihil consensus bonorum omnium, nihil hic munitissimus habendi senatus locus, nihil horum ora vultusque moverunt? patere tua consilia non sentis? constrictam jam omnium horum conscientia teneri conjuratio nem tuam non vides? quid proxima, quid superiore nocte egeris, ubi fueris, quos convocaveris, quid consilii ceperis, quem nostrum ignorare arbitraris? O tempora, o mores! Senatus hoc intelligit, consul vidit: hic tamen vivit. Vivit? imo vero etiam in senatum venit: fit publici consilii particeps: notat et designat oculis ad cædem unumquemque nostrum. Nos autem viri fortes satisfacere reipublicæ videmur, si istius furorem ac tela vitemus. Ad mortem te, Catilina, duci jussu consulis, jam pridem oporte-

ABCDEFGHIJKLMNOPQRSTUVWXYZÆŒ

V. FIGGINS.

Minion, No. 4.

Quousque tandem abutere, Catilina, patientia nostra? quamdiu nos etiam furor iste tuus eludet? quem ad finem sese effrenata jactabit audacia? nihilne te nocturnum præsidium palatii, nihil urbis vigiliæ, nihil timor populi, nihil consensus bonorum omnium, nihil hic munitissimus habendi senatus locus ni hil horum ora vultusque moverunt? patere tua consilia non sentis? constrictam jam omnium horum conscientia teneri conjurationem tuam non vides? quid proxima, quid superiore, nocte egeris, ubi fueris, quos convocaveris, quid consilii ceperis, quem nostrum ignorare arbitraris? O tempora, o mores! Senatus hoc intelligit, consul vidit: hic tamen vivit. Vivit? imo vero etiam in senatum venit: fit publici consilii particeps: notat et designat oculis ad cædem unumquemque nostrum. Nos autem viri fortes satisfacere reipublicæ videmur, si istius furorem ac tela vitemus. Ad mortem te, Catilina, duci jussu consulis, jam pridem oportebat: in te conferri pestem istam, quam tu in

ABCDEFGHIJKLMNOPQRSTUVWXYZÆŒ
1234567890

Quousque tandem abutere, Catilina, patientia nostra? quamdiu nos etiam furor iste tuus eludet? quem ad finem sese effrenata jactabit audacia? nihilne te nocturnum præsidium palatii, nihil urbis vigiliæ, nihil timor populi, nihil consensus bonorum omnium, nihil hic munitissimus habendi senatus locus, nihil horum ora vultusque moverunt? patere tua consilia non sentis? constrictam jam omnium horum conscientia teneri conjurationem tuam non vides? quid proxima, quid superiore, nocte egeris, ubi fueris, quos convocaveris, quid consilii ceperis, quem nostrum ignorare arbitraris? O tempora, o mores! Senatus hoc intelligit, consul vidit: hic tamen vivit. Vivit? imo vero etiam in senatum venit: fit publici consilii particeps: notat et designat oculis ad cædem unumquemque nostrum. Nos autem viri fortes satisfacere reipublicæ videmur, si istius furorem ac tela vitemus. Ad mortem te, Catilina, duci jussu consulis jam pridem oportebat: in te conferri pestem istam, quam tu in nos omnes jam-

ABCDEFGHIJKLMNOPQRSTUVWXYZÆŒ

Minion, No. 5.

Quousque tandem abutere, Catilina, patientia nostra? quamdiu nos etiam furor iste tuus eludet? quem ad finem sese effrenata jactabit audacia? nihilne te nocturnum præsidium palatii, nihil urbis vigiliæ, nihil timor populi, nihil consensus bonorum omnium, nihil hic munitissimus habendi senatus locus? nihil horum ora vultusque moverunt? patere tua consilia non sentis constrictam jam omnium horum conscientia teneri conjurationem tuam non vides? quid proxima, quid superiore nocte egeris, ubi fueris, quos convocaveris, quid consilii ceperis, quem nostrum ignorare arbitraris? O tempora, o mores! Senatus hoc intelligit, consul vidit: hic tamen vivit. Vivit? imo vero etiam in senatum venit: fit publici consilii particeps: notat et designat oculis ad cædem unumquemque nostrum. Nos autem viri fortes satisfacere reipublicæ videmur, si istius furorem ac tela vitemus. Ad mortem te, Catilina, duci jussu consulis jam pridem oportebat: in te conferri pestem istam,

ABCDEFGHIJKLMNOPQRSTUVWXYZÆŒ
1234567890

Quousque tandem abutere, Catilina, patientia nostra? quamdiu nos etiam furor iste tuus eludet? quem ad finem sese effrenata jactabit audacia? nihil ne te nocturnum præsidium palatii, nihil urbis vigiliæ, nihil timor populi, nihil consensus bonorum omnium, nihil hic munitissimus habendi senatus locus? nihil horum ora vultusque moverunt? patere tua consilia non sentis? constrictam jam omnium horum conscientia teneri conjurationem tuam non vides quid proxima, quid superiore nocte egeris, ubi fueris, quos convocaveris, quid consilii ceperis, quem nostrum ignorare arbitraris? O tempora, o mores! Senatus hoc intelligit, consul vidit: hic tamen vivit. Vivit? imo vero etiam in senatum venit: fit publici consilii particeps: notat et designat oculis ad cædem unumquemque nostrum. Nos autem viri fortes satisfacere reipublicæ videmur si istius furorem ac tela vitemus. Ad mortem te Catilina duci jussu consulis jam pridem oportebat: in te conferri pestem istam quam tu in nos om

ABCDEFGHIJKLMNOPQRSTUVWXYZÆŒ

V. FIGGINS.

Nonpariel, No. 2. on Pearl Body.

DEARLY beloved brethren, the Scripture moveth us in sundry places to acknowledge and confess our manifold sins and wickedness; and that we should not dissemble nor cloke them before the face of Almighty God our heavenly Father; but confess them with an humble, lowly, penitent, and obedient heart; to the end that we may obtain forgiveness of the same, by his infinite goodness and mercy. And although we ought at all times humbly to acknowledge our sins before God; yet ought we most chiefly so to do, when we assemble and meet together to render thanks for the great benefits that we have received at his hands, to set forth his most worthy praise, to hear his most holy word, and to ask those things which are requisite and necessary, as well for the body as the soul. Wherefore, I pray and beseech you, as many as are here present, to accompany me with a pure heart, and humble voice, unto the throne of the heavenly grace, saying after me;

Pearl.

NOW his parents went to Jerusalem every year at the feast of the passover. And when he was twelve years old, they went up to Jerusalem, after the custom of the feast. And when they had fulfilled the days, as they returned, the child Jesus tarried behind in Jerusalem; and Joseph and his mother knew not of it. But they, supposing him to have been in the company, went a day's journey, and they sought him among their kinsfolk and acquaintance. And when they found him not, they turned back again to Jerusalem, seeking him. And it came to pass, that after three days they found him in the temple, sitting in the midst of the doctors, both hearing them, and asking them questions. And all that heard him were astonished at his understanding and answers. And when they saw him, they were amazed: and his mother said unto him, Son, why hast thou thus dealt with us? Behold, thy father and I have sought thee sorrowing. And he said unto them, How is it that ye sought me? wist ye not that I must be about my Father's business? And they understood not the saying which he spake unto them. And he went down with them, and came to Nazareth, and was subject unto them: but his mother kept all these sayings in her heart. And Jesus increased in wisdom and stature, and in favour with God and man.

Diamond.

15 ¶ O LORD, thou knowest: remember me, and visit me, and revenge me of my persecutors; take me not away in thy longsuffering: know that for thy sake I have suffered rebuke.

16 Thy words were found, and I did eat them; and thy word was unto me the joy and rejoicing of mine heart: for I am called by thy name, O LORD God of hosts.

17 I sat not in the assembly of the mockers, nor rejoiced; I sat alone because of thy hand: for thou hast filled me with indignation.

18 Why is my pain perpetual, and my wound incurable, which refuseth to be healed? wilt thou be altogether unto me as a liar, and as waters that fail?

19 ¶ Therefore thus saith the LORD, If thou return, then will I bring thee again, and thou shalt stand before me: and if thou take forth the precious from the vile, thou shalt be as my mouth: let them return unto thee; but return not thou unto them.

20 And I will make thee unto this people a fenced brasen wall: and they shall fight against thee, but they shall not prevail against thee: for I am with thee to save thee and to deliver thee, saith the LORD.

21 And I will deliver thee out of the hand of the wicked, and I will redeem thee out of the hand of the terrible.

8 Thou shalt not also go into the house of feasting, to sit with them to eat and to drink.

9 For thus saith the LORD of hosts, the God of Israel; Behold, I will cause to cease out of this place in your eyes, and in your days, the voice of mirth, and the voice of gladness, the voice of the bridegroom, and the voice of the bride.

10 ¶ And it shall come to pass, when thou shalt shew this people all these words, and they shall say unto thee, Wherefore hath the LORD pronounced all this great evil against us? or what is our iniquity? or what is our sin that we have committed against the LORD our God?

11 Then shalt thou say unto them, Because your fathers have forsaken me, saith the LORD, and have walked after other gods, and have served them, and have worshipped them, and have forsaken me, and have not kept my law;

12 And ye have done worse than your fathers; for, behold, ye walk every one after the imagination of his evil heart, that they may not hearken unto me:

13 Therefore will I cast you out of this land into a land that ye know not, neither ye nor your fathers; and there shall ye serve other gods day and night; where I will not shew you favour.

14 ¶ Therefore, behold, the days come

V. FIGGINS.

TWO LINE, No.2.

GREAT PRIMER.

ABCDEFGHIJKLM
NOPQRSTUVWXY,

ENGLISH.

ABCDEFGHIJKLMNOP
QRSTUVWXYZÆŒ.

V.FIGGINS.

PICA.

ABCDEFGHIJKLMNOP

SMALL PICA.

ABCDEFGHIJKLMNOPQRSTUV

LONG PRIMER.

ABCDEFGHIJKLMNOPQRSTUVW

BURGEOIS.

ABCDEFGHIJKLMNOPQRSTUVWXY

V. FIGGINS.

Five Lines Pica.

And be it further hereby enacted, T MABCDEFGH

Figgins.

Five Lines Pica.

And be it further hereby enacted

ABCDEFG
MNOPQRS

Figgins.

And be it further hereby enac
ted that the Mayors Bailiffs
or other head Officers, of e=
very Town and place corpo
rate, and City, within this
Realm being Justice or Jus
tices of Peace, shall have the

And be it further hereby enacted that
the Mayors Bailiffs, or other head
Officers, of every Town and place
corporate, and City, within, this
Realm being Justice or Justices of
Peace, shall have the same authori
ty by virtue of this Act within the
limits and precincts of their Juris

And be it further hereby enacted, That
the Mayors, Bailiffs, and other head Of
ficers of every Town and place corpo=
rate, and City within this Realm, being
Justice or Justices of Peace, shall have
the same authority by virtue of this Act
within the limits and precincts of their
Jurisdictions, as well out of Sessions
as at their Sessions, if they hold any,
as is herein limited, prescribed and ap=

V.FIGGINS.

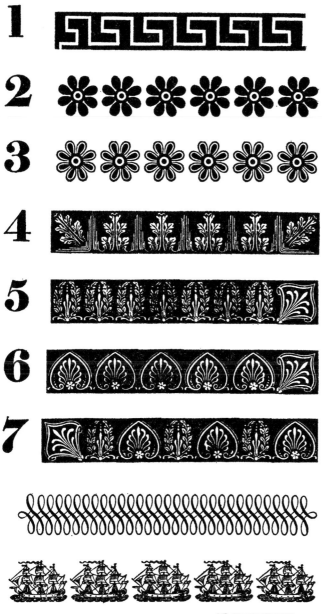

V.FIGGINS.

8

TWO LINES ENGLISH.

TWO LINES PICA.

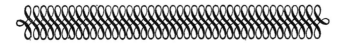

DOUBLE PICA.

V. FIGGINS.

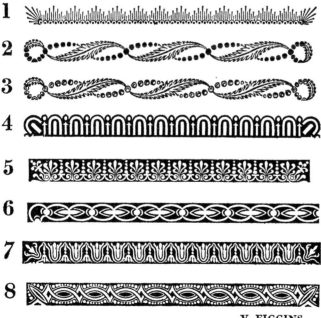

3

4

5

6

7

8

9

GREAT PRIMER.

1

2

3

4

5

6

7

8

V. FIGGINS.

9
10
11

TWO LINES BURGEOIS.

ENGLISH.

1
2
3
4
5
6
7
8
9
10
11
12
13
14

V. FIGGINS.

15

16

17

18

19

20

1

2

3

4

5

6

7

8

9

10

11

12

1

2

3

4

V. FIGGINS.

5
6
7
8
9
10
11
12
13
14
15

1
2
3
4
5
6
7
8
9
10
11
12
13
14
15
16
17
18

V. FIGGINS.

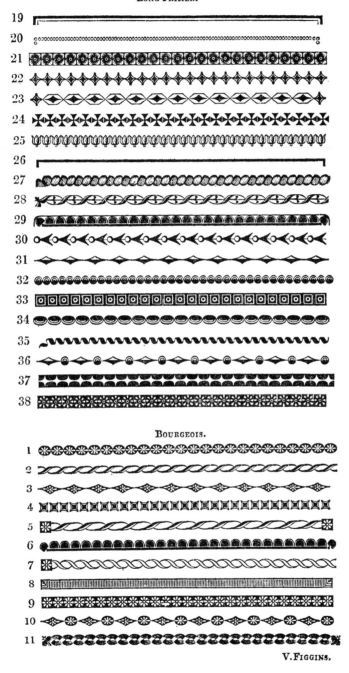

Bourgeois.

V. Figgins.

1

2

3

4

5

6

7

8

9

10

11

12

13

14

15

16

17

18

19

20

21

22

23

24

25

26

27

28

29

30

31

MINION.

1

2

3

4

V. **FIGGINS.**

MINION.

5
6
7
8
9
10

NONPARIEL.

1
2
3
4
5
6
7
8
9
10
11
12
13
14
15
16

PEARL.

1
2
3
4
5
6
7
8
9
10
11
12
13
14
15
16
17
18
19

V. FIGGINS.

An Appendix

of three leaves of display types which appear in the Oxford copy, here ascribed to the year 1817. They include the first showing of slab-serifed Antique, now known as Egyptian. See also Nicolette Gray, *Nineteenth Century Ornamented Types*, London, 1938

FOUR LINES PICA ORNAMENTED No.2.

ABCDEFGHIJ
KLMNOPQRS.

TWO LINES ENGLISH, ORNAMENTED.

ABCDEFGHIJKLMNOPQR
BY PRIVATE CONTRACT,
VINCENT FIGGINS.